The Science of Commerce

# SUCCEEDING IN THE CHANGED MEDICAL DEVICE MARKET

ECON Publishing

Ryan Saadi | Daniel Grima | Nicole Ferko

ECON Publishing, New Jersey, USA,
circulation@econpublishing.com

Ryan Saadi, Daniel Grima, Nicole Ferko
The Science of Commerce
Succeeding in the Changed Medical Device Market
ECON Publishing, 2012, 118 pages

Printed in Canada.

ISBN 978-0-9856491-0-4

For Emily, Charlotte, Alicia, and Ben –

"Make your dreams one size too big,
so that you can grow into them."

"This comprehensive yet concisely-written book offers solutions for industry executives navigating through the complicated terrain of today's market access hurdles. These solutions have originated through an innovative, strategic approach and are well-supported by contemporary evidence"

*– Dr. Campbell Rogers, Chief Medical Officer, HeartFlow, Inc.*

"Succeeding in the Changed Medical Device Market methodically embraces the shift to a value-driven market with the goal of optimizing health in a time of constrained resources. The authors have combined their complementary and considerable experience in health outcomes, reimbursement, health policy and pricing, as well as Ryan's experience in all sectors of the global health care system to develop this forward-thinking and didactic book for those needing to understand the market access landscape for medical technologies"

*– Dr. Georges Gemayel, Chairman of Syndexa Pharmaceuticals and Vascular Magnetics Inc.*

"Dr. Ryan Saadi and co-authors have intelligently captured the new and evolving requirements for market access of medical technologies. Their book provides an evidence-based thought process that serves to provoke innovative change in a time of exceptional need"

*– Dr. Bruce Cooper, Head, Global Medical Affairs, Hoffmann-La Roche Ltd*

## ACKNOWLEDGMENTS

The authors express their sincere gratitude to Harman, Judy, Ray, and Shafiq for their review and helpful commentary regarding draft versions of this book. The authors would also like to thank Sarah Hollmann for her support in developing illustrations and editing this book, as well as Cheryl, Lisa, and Melissa for their contributions to its content and concepts.

## DISCLOSURES

Dr. Ryan Saadi discloses that the content of this book represents his personal views, not the views of Johnson & Johnson (J&J), nor any of J&J subsidiaries, nor any of his former employers. These personal views reflect Dr. Saadi's assimilated knowledge and experience of close to 20 years in the global health care sector.

Daniel Grima is a shareholder and employee, and Nicole Ferko is an employee, of Cornerstone Research Group Inc, which provides research and consulting services to the medical device and pharmaceutical industry. The content of the book represents their personal views and reflects their experience and accumulated knowledge.

# PREFACE

Health care innovation has offered tremendous value for patients by improving survival, decreasing symptoms, and providing hope. While innovation will remain the key to success for health care companies, rising health care costs have created pressures on spending that have placed payers and purchasers as the new gatekeepers of access to innovative health care technologies. The marketplace continues to evolve, with possibly the most profound changes occurring in the United States.

If medical device and other health care companies are to thrive in this new market paradigm, development and commercialization strategies need to evolve to satisfy the expectations of this changed customer base, which includes physicians, payers, purchasers, and patients. Numerous medical device companies have failed to live up to market expectations. These failures could have been prevented with a clear understanding of both the changes in how products gain access to the market as well as the influence of the new device customers. Notably, current demands on medical device companies mirror those previously occurring within the pharmaceutical industry. Device companies can gain valuable knowledge from these earlier experiences, as well as thrive in this new health care environment.

We wrote this book not only to inspire and inform change, but most importantly to deliver proven solutions for the evolving medical device industry. These solutions are built on our extensive understanding of current challenges and our decades of industry experience and knowledge. In this book, we elaborate on the complex changes in the health care market observed in the past decades, and demystify the methods and vocabulary used to define product value. The book brings together our complementary experience, using insights into the intricate inter-relationships between all sectors of the U.S. and global health care systems to deliver solutions for achieving successful market access.

The book draws heavily from Ryan's almost 20 years in leadership positions in hospital administration, managed care, and the pharmaceutical, biotechnology, and medical device industries to present a vision regarding how the medical device industry needs to adapt to an evidence-based, value-focused market. His industry insight is complemented by Daniel's and Nicole's long-standing strategic and methodological expertise in health economics and market access within increasingly restrictive reimbursement environments. For a vast array of health care technologies, these authors have proven their skills to assess, develop, and communicate customer-specific product value arguments that ensure continued patient access. A large part of their success is based on their in-depth knowledge of the relevant value metrics that currently hold stakeholder interest, along with their ability to simply and effectively communicate complex topics.

The solutions presented within this book were designed for quick adoption by the medical device industry, thereby enabling continued successful market access. Although short-term financial goals remain important, long-term survival is critical; accordingly, the solutions were built on a framework that encourages sustained adaptation to ongoing change. Most important – beyond company success – readers must be aware of the broader advantages of adapting to the new environment, including delivering profits to company stockholders, maintaining high technology jobs, sustaining product innovation, and above all, improving health care through continued patient access.

The time to change is now. To succeed, medical device companies must seek innovative and sustainable solutions. As Albert Einstein stated: "Problems cannot be solved by the same level of thinking that created them."

**RS, DG, NF**

# ACRONYMS AND ABBREVIATIONS

| | |
|---|---|
| **AHCRP** | Agency for Health Care Policy and Research |
| **AHRQ** | Agency for Healthcare Research and Quality |
| **AMCP** | Academy of Managed Care Pharmacy |
| **ARRA** | American Recovery and Reinvestment Act of 2009 |
| **BIA** | budget impact analysis |
| **BMS** | bare-metal stent |
| **CADTH** | Canadian Agency for Drugs and Technologies in Health |
| **CCOHTA** | Canadian Coordinating Office for Health Technology Assessment |
| **CDN** | Canadian |
| **CE** | Conformité Européenne |
| **CEA** | cost-effectiveness analysis |
| **CED** | coverage with evidence development |
| **CEM** | cost-effectiveness model |
| **CER** | comparative effectiveness research |
| **CME** | continuing medical education |
| **CMS** | U.S. Centers for Medicare & Medicaid Services |
| **CPT** | Current Procedural Terminology |
| **DES** | drug-eluting stent |
| **DRG** | diagnosis-related group |
| **EU** | European Union |
| **EUnetHTA** | European network for Health Technology Assessment |
| **FDA** | U.S. Food and Drug Administration |
| **GDP** | gross domestic product |
| **GOVT** | government |
| **GVD** | global value dossier |
| **HE** | health economics |
| **HRQOL** | health-related quality of life |
| **HTA** | health technology assessment |
| **ICD** | International Classification of Diseases |
| **ICER** | incremental cost-effectiveness ratio |
| **INESSS** | Institut nationale d'excellence en santé et en services sociaux |

| | |
|---|---|
| **IOM** | Institute of Medicine of the National Academies |
| **IQWiG** | Institut für Qualität und Wirtschaftlichkeit im Gesundheits-wesen (Institute for Quality and Efficiency in Healthcare) |
| **ITC** | indirect treatment comparison |
| **MTC** | mixed treatment comparison |
| **MTEP** | Medical Technologies Evaluation Program |
| **NHS** | UK National Health Service |
| **NICE** | National Institute for Health and Clinical Excellence |
| **NPAF** | National Patient Advocate Foundation |
| **OECD** | Organisation for Economic Co-operation and Development |
| **OTA** | U.S. Office of Technology Assessment |
| **PBAC** | Pharmaceutical Benefits Advisory Committee |
| **PCI** | percutaneous coronary intervention |
| **PCORI** | Patient-Centered Outcomes Research Institute |
| **PMA** | Pre-Market Approval |
| **PPACA** | Patient Protection and Affordable Care Act |
| **PPI** | physician preference item |
| **PRO** | patient-reported outcome |
| **QALY** | quality-adjusted life year |
| **R&D** | research and development |
| **RCT** | randomized controlled trial |
| **ROI** | return on investment |
| **SBU** | Swedish Council on Health Technology Assessment in Health Care |
| **TAC** | technology assessment committee |
| **UK** | United Kingdom |
| **U.S.** | United States |
| **USD** | U.S. dollar |
| **VA** | U.S. Department of Veterans Affairs |
| **VAC** | value analysis committee |
| **VBP** | value-based pricing |

# CHAPTER 1

# Introduction – Capitalizing on Change

The concept that "change is the only constant in the universe" is attributed to the Greek philosopher Heraclitus. In business, as well as nature, this concept is often expressed as "adapt or die," or more positively, "adapt and thrive." This business philosophy mandates constant vigilance to recognize and adapt to changes in the marketplace. Businesses that heed this advice gain a competitive edge in the marketplace, especially in times of profound change.

The medical device industry is growing rapidly, with an estimated market of $104 billion in the United States and €64 billion in Europe.[1] At the same time, health care costs have been rising exponentially, with much discussion and implementation measures focused on the industry's sustainability. In the United States, for instance, health care costs were approximately 17% of the gross domestic product (GDP) in 2009, up from 7% in 1970, with expenditures for medical devices representing close to 1% of the GDP.[1,2] Studies in the United States and Europe have concluded that technological change related to medical devices and pharmaceutical technologies is a much stronger driver of growth in health spending than the trend toward aging societies.[2] As a result, medical device manufacturers are currently facing increased pricing and reimbursement pressures that are impeding market access success. This shift mirrors what has been occurring in the pharmaceutical industry over the past decade and reflects a new reality.

Essentially, market access of medical technologies, such as devices, has become highly contingent on coverage and reimbursement by payers, who are the new gatekeepers to the marketplace – a role previously dominated by physicians. While physician demand is still necessary, it is no longer sufficient for successful market access. In brief, the *Pulse of the Industry: Medical Technology Report 2011* notes: "Payers – both public and private – have seen their budgets squeezed and are, in turn, pressuring medical technology companies to demonstrate how their products improve health outcomes for patients and efficiently use health care resources. Even if clinical trials are not required to get a product approved, payers will increasingly focus on post-marketing data on the comparative effectiveness of different interventions."[3]

In essence, if the last era of the pharmaceutical industry was referred to as the Blockbuster Era, the current era, which focuses on product value, can be referred to as the Value Era. In this challenged environment, the term *market access* needs to be viewed within the industry as a cross-functional, multidisciplinary approach involving the optimization of market uptake by demonstrating and communicating the complete *product value proposition,* which is tailored to today's relevant customer needs. Companies that can adapt to new market access requirements and capitalize on the opportunities these changes provide will be the market leaders in the coming decades.

This book, focusing on the United States and Europe, examines how changes in the health care system have created the foundations of the Value Era. This introduction provides the framework of the book, detailing the context of each of the chapters.

*Chapter 2* examines the evolution of the Value Era for health care technologies in general and describes the new key customers, methods of restricting product access, and metrics used to measure product value (e.g., comparative effectiveness, cost-effectiveness analysis). These concepts are placed in the context of a timeline that illustrates their increasing utilization and importance over the past 40 years.

*Chapter 3* applies the Value Era concepts to the medical device industry. It provides the rationale and its underlying evidence that new processes are relevant, and new customers (e.g., hospital purchasers) need to be targeted for medical device manufacturers to succeed today.

This chapter emphasizes how decision-making power is shifting from physicians/surgeons to hospital purchasers, and illustrates this shift through strategies and processes (e.g., hospital technology assessment committees) that are increasingly being utilized to efficiently purchase medical devices. Several examples in the chapter substantiate these needs, including surveys of medical device companies and hospital decision makers, as well as Centers for Medicare & Medicaid Services and state Medicaid studies regarding medical device scenarios.

*Chapter 4* and *Chapter 5* are the focus of the book. Given the evidence of the substantial challenges facing the industry, these chapters provide an integrated solution for medical device companies to grow and achieve market access success in this new environment. This solution involves ongoing assessment starting at the early stages of product development, a comprehensive evidence generation phase, the development of communication tools, and a targeted system for communicating product value to all customers. The chapters detail relevant questions that companies need to consider during various phases of product development and marketing, and incorporate examples to expand upon the types of evidence required to demonstrate the complete value proposition. The integrated solution is placed in the context of a Health Economics (HE) team within the industry, which is imperative to successful market access and is required for implementing several of the recommended tasks. In addition, cross-functional alignment of the HE team with Research & Development and Commercial teams is necessary to optimize product strategy for payers and purchasers.

*Chapter 6*, the last chapter, provides some additional considerations for adapting to the new market demands. Recognizing that the proposed solution will need to be uniquely adapted to different company situations and that such adaptation will present significant challenges; the chapter provides final thoughts for handling this variability and overcoming some of the pitfalls that may prevent successful implementation.

---

1 Schreyögg J, et al. Balancing adoption and affordability of medical devices in Europe. *Health Policy* 2009; 92(2-3):218-24.
2 Organisation for Economic Co-operation and Development. Social expenditure: Aggregated data. OECD Social Expenditure Statistics (database). 2011.
3 Ernst & Young. Pulse of the industry: Medical technology report. EYGM Limited. 2011; (FN0008) 1107-1271824_SF. Available at: http://www.ey.com/Publication/vwLUAssets/Pulse_of_the_industry/$FILE/Pulse-of-the-industry.pdf. [Accessed on: May 04, 2012]

# CHAPTER 2

# Transitioning from the Blockbuster Era to the Value Era

## KEY MESSAGE:

Rising health care costs have led to changes in how budget expenditures are assessed and allocated, introducing a Value Era of cost containment. In this new era, payers act as gatekeepers to the marketplace, and physicians' awareness of a new product is no longer sufficient to ensure its adoption. This transition is well established globally and is gaining momentum in the U.S. market. This changing environment offers both challenges and opportunities for the medical device and pharmaceutical industries. By considering the value metrics payers will use, companies can create research, development, and commercialization processes that optimize their products' potential for successful market access.

## CONCEPTS DISCUSSED:

- Growing health care concerns as the fundamental driver of the Value Era.
- Payers as gatekeepers to access of health care technologies.
- Access restrictions (e.g., formularies) based on perceived product value.
- Impact of access restrictions on sales.

Historically, both the pharmaceutical and the medical device industries generated success based on the principles of creating safe products that were at least as effective as those of their competitors. At times, they leapfrogged the competition with innovation, such as with the introduction of drug-eluting stents for coronary artery disease, when the standard of care was bare-metal stents. Once a product obtained regulatory approval, the emphasis switched to sales and marketing activities, which created product awareness[a] and generated demand. Marketing activities primarily focused – and continue to focus – on clinicians who prescribe or utilize a health care technology.[b] Within this context, there were few barriers to market success beyond regulatory requirements and competition. This philosophy has now fundamentally changed.

## 2.1 | Growing Health Care Budgets and Growing Concerns

The unprecedented success of the medical technology industry in creating innovative products for addressing unmet medical needs has given rise to a new challenge: health care budgets have experienced continuous and unsustainable growth. For example, in the United States, health care costs were approximately 7% of gross domestic product (GDP) in 1970; in 2009, they represented 17.4% of GDP.[1] Similar increases, though less dramatic, have been observed globally in all major economies *(Figure 2.1)*.[1]

The causes of this health care spending boom are beyond the scope of this book; however a brief discussion can be insightful.

- First, one cannot ignore the innovation of the pharmaceutical and medical device industries. Although astounding, the growth

---

[a] **Product awareness:** Can be defined as influencer (i.e., those who have influence over potential buyers/customers) and customer recognition of the existence, availability, and value of a health care technology.

[b] **Health care technologies:** Any method or intervention that is employed to provide positive health outcomes. The technology may contribute to disease prevention or diagnosis, treatment options, or rehabilitation. Accordingly, drugs, devices, diagnostics, equipment, and procedures may all be considered health care technologies.

**FIGURE 2.1 |** Total expenditure on health, as a percentage of GDP, for several countries.[1]

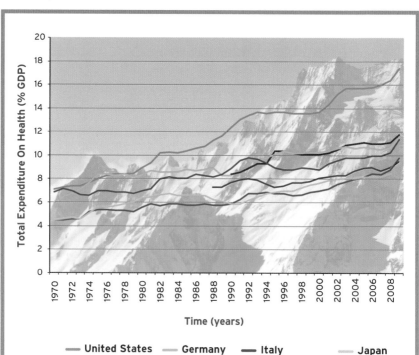

in health care spending is a testament to the innovations made by researchers and clinicians. One challenge of the success of the Blockbuster Era is that many common diseases are now well treated, which makes future breakthroughs more difficult to achieve. This in turn has raised the *costs of product development.* For instance, over the previous 20 years, the average cost of developing a drug has risen at a rate 7.4% higher than inflation.[2]

- A second factor driving health care costs is that groundbreaking discoveries in medical treatment have led to substantial *increases in the life expectancy* of the general population. Previously fatal conditions are now associated with significant life expectancies and are managed as chronic conditions. For example, many cancers are now managed using long-term multi-therapy treatment protocols. Upstream, the availability of more first-line therapies raises the upfront costs of treating newly diagnosed patients. Downstream, patients with severe conditions live longer through the use of innovative chronic therapies.

- At the same time that health care options have grown, the demographics in many industrialized countries have shifted to *older populations,* which have *higher-than-average health care usage.* For example, the proportion of the U.S. population above age 45 was 30.5% in 1970, compared to 36.4% in 2000.[3] This age shift is important, since nearly one-third of lifetime health care expenditures occur in middle age, and nearly half during the senior years.[4]

- Finally, spending is being driven by the movement to *personalized medicine,* where therapies are targeted to individual patients or patient subgroups with specific genetic profiles.[5] These targeted products have the benefit of avoiding treatment of patients who would not respond, but have the challenge of a smaller target population. This necessitates *higher pricing* to provide sufficient revenue to justify product development. Such targeting is most evident in areas of rare diseases and oncology, where payer concern over pricing of products has been very vocal.

The rise in health care spending has been mirrored by discussion about its sustainability in both academic journals and the popular media. A sample of *TIME Magazine* articles provides a window into these increasing concerns *(Figure 2.2).*[6] These articles initially focused on documenting the rise in spending and its root causes. During the 1980s and 1990s, the spending debate shifted to questions regarding the value of increased spending versus options for controlling spending while maximizing population health.

**FIGURE 2.2 |** Sample TIME Magazine topics covered between 1967 and 2004 reflect growing concerns about health care costs and the need for solutions. This sample does not include the numerous articles reflecting the recent heightened debate over U.S. health care reform.

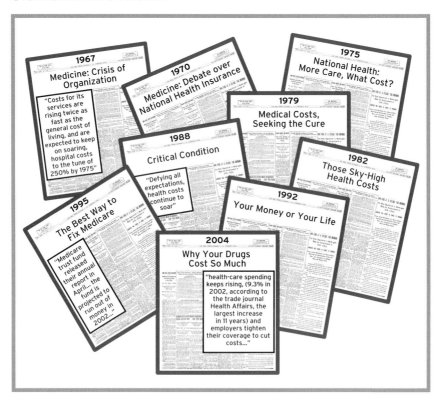

## 2.2 | The Emergence of the Value Era

The growth in health care spending and the vocal widespread debate of its impacts gave birth to the Value Era. The focus during this era expands beyond questions of efficacy and safety for a single product (typically versus placebo), to questions regarding the comparative clinical benefit of a product versus a wide range of alternative products, as well as the product's cost-effectiveness (its value for money spent)

**TABLE 2.1 | Questions and hurdles that characterize the Blockbuster and Value Eras.**

| | Blockbuster Era | Value Era |
|---|---|---|
| **Data Questions** | • Is it efficacious and safe versus a reasonable clinical trial comparator? | • Is it more efficacious and safe versus all reasonable treatment alternatives?<br>• Is it good value for money[c] (i.e., cost-effective)?<br>• Is it affordable[d]? |
| **Hurdles to Market Access Success** | • Regulatory approval<br>• Product awareness / commercial activities | • Regulatory approval<br>• Product awareness / commercial activities<br>• Product reimbursement[e] |

and overall affordability *(Table 2.1)*. In this era, being efficacious and well marketed is no longer sufficient for market success. A product must also provide good value compared to its competition, and must meet customer expectations of value to achieve coverage and reimbursement under government, private, and hospital product formularies.

The search for products that can address the new concerns and hurdles of the Value Era has led to numerous changes in how health care is managed, has brought to the forefront new methods for assessing value, and has resulted in the emergence of stakeholders who can dramatically affect a product's success. The key changes in terms of players, processes, and methods that describe the Value Era are summarized in *Figure 2.3* and discussed in more detail later in this chapter.

---

[c] **Value for money:** The general concept of whether the added clinical benefit of a product can be obtained for a reasonable added cost. This assessment uses the value metric of cost-effectiveness analysis which is later defined.

[d] **Affordable:** Refers to whether the payer or purchaser has sufficient budget to accommodate the use of a therapy in all patients eligible for therapy. This assessment often uses the value metric of budget impact analysis which is later defined.

[e] **Reimbursement:** A term describing how payers pay for the items or services provided by medical professionals. Reimbursement can be broken down into three components: coverage, coding, and payment. Coverage can be referred to as the determination by payers regarding whether, and to what extent, they will pay for a service, process, or product.

**FIGURE 2.3 |** Foundation and evolution of the Value Era.

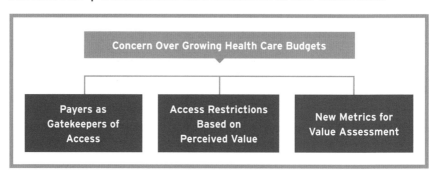

## 2.3 | The Emergence of Payers as Gatekeepers to Market Access

### 2.3.1 GLOBAL PERSPECTIVE

Growing concern over health care spending and strengthened political will to address the issue shifted the debate to: Who will act as the spending gatekeepers? How will they make decisions? Safeguarding spending has been the topic of endless political and academic debate. Globally, payers have emerged as the stakeholders most commonly charged with the task of limiting health care spending while maximizing public health. The logic of selecting payers as the gatekeepers is simple: they represent the point of distribution of health care budgets.

Payers use a broad range of systems and tools to control spending, which can generally be broken into a number of categories *(Table 2.2)*. The majority of these tools focus on restricted access of prescribers, purchasers, or patients to a technology, or reductions in the price of the technology.

Making such coverage decisions requires a thorough review of the clinical, epidemiological, and economic outcomes literature. These evaluations require specialized teams with a broad knowledge-base and defensible systems for data identification, review, analysis, and reporting. To meet this new challenge, two groups have evolved:

**TABLE 2.2** | Access and price restrictions used
by payers across several countries

| | |
|---|---|
| **Restricted Access** | • Lack of coverage: With a selective formulary, funding is restricted to products included in the formulary. Other products are not eligible for funding. This system is common in Europe, Canada and Australia in both public and private systems.<br><br>• Dispensing or administering therapies only through authorized pharmacies and physicians to control access and inappropriate prescribing. |
| **Limited Use / Prior Authorization** | • Limited-use populations: Use of a product is restricted to patients who meet criteria that are typically more restrictive than those on the product label. These populations may include high-risk subgroups or patients who have not had success with less expensive generic products. This system is common in Europe, Canada, and Australia, and is becoming more common in the United States. For example, restrictions based on prior authorization are being considered for antipsychotics in the United States.[7]<br><br>• Quantity limitations to restrict overall use. |
| **Financial Disincentives** | • Co-payments: Patients must pay a portion of the cost of the product. Lower co-payments are assigned to products preferred by payers; common globally, but prevalent in United States. |
| **Price Reductions** | • Payers may negotiate rebates to lower the unit costs of products. This is common in the United States and has been gaining prominence with public payers in Canada and Europe. |
| **Risk Sharing Agreements** | • Performance-based agreements: These link a product's coverage, price, and/or revenue to future performance. A range of schemes exist, but a common system is rebating the cost of the product for patients who do not respond to therapy.[8,9]<br><br>• Evidence development agreements: These allow funding for a limited period, during which the manufacturer must gather further evidence of the product's effectiveness.[9] The Centers for Medicare & Medicaid Services' (CMS's) coverage with evidence development is an example.[10] |

- Many governments have established specialized groups to assess product value and issue guidance to payers. Often these groups, which may exist at a national or regional level, are autonomous from payers in order to reduce potential bias.

- In conjunction with these independent groups, payers have developed internal resources to assess and review guidance reports from these independent agencies and/or conduct their own independent reviews, as well as provide recommendations on coverage. The teams that conduct such evaluations go by various names including Health Technology Assessment (HTA) Committees, Evidence Review Committees, and Reimbursement Advisory Boards. Examples of such groups are included in *Table 2.3.*

**TABLE 2.3 | Global examples of independent and payer-based groups that assess product value**

### U.S. Examples

- The CMS: various groups, including the Medicare Coverage Division, Medicare Evidence Development and Coverage Advisory Committee, and state Medicaid groups.
- State health agencies, such as the Washington State Health Care Authority's Health Technology Assessment Program.
- Department of Veterans Affairs (VA) Pharmacy Benefits Management Strategic Healthcare Group.
- Academic groups, such as the Oregon Health and Sciences University's Drug Effectiveness Review Program, which works with numerous state Medicaid agencies.
- Private payers, such as Blue Cross and Blue Shield Association's Technology Evaluation Center (TEC) and the WellPoint Health Technology Assessment Group.
- Government agencies, such as the Office of Technology Assessment and the Agency for Healthcare Research and Quality.
- Private technology assessment groups, such as Hayes Inc. and ECRI Institute.
- Hospital committees, such as technology assessment committees and HTA or reimbursement advisory boards.

### Global Examples

National agencies, such as:

- The Canadian Agency for Drugs and Technologies in Health (CADTH).
- The United Kingdom's (UK's) National Institute for Health and Clinical Excellence (NICE).
- Germany's Institute for Quality and Efficiency in Healthcare (IQWiG).
- Australia's Pharmaceutical Benefits Advisory Committee (PBAC).
- The Swedish Council on Health Technology Assessment (SBU).

Regional agencies, such as:

- Provincial agencies in Canada, including the Institut national d'excellence en santé et en services sociaux (INESSS) (in Quebec) and the Committee to Evaluate Drugs (in Ontario).
- National Health Service (NHS) trusts (primacy care, acute, ambulance, secondary care, and mental health) in the UK.

International agencies, such as:

- The European network for Health Technology Assessment (EUnetHTA), which fosters cooperation on HTA in Europe.
- The Cochrane Collaboration, an international association for meta-analysis of clinical studies.

The emergence of payer groups, assessment agencies, and new evaluation methods started to gain momentum in the 1990s globally *(Figure 2.4)* and a little later in the United States *(Figure 2.5)*. Initially, the primary focus was on health care programs (for example, fluoride in drinking water) and pharmaceutical products, rather than medical devices and diagnostics. In fact, most international guidelines for economic evaluation have been developed with pharmaceuticals in mind. Recently, however, there has been growing discussion and implementation of medical device HTA in a number of jurisdictions. For example, the UK recently established the Medical Technologies Evaluation Program, which specifically focuses on the review of devices and diagnostics as part of the NICE process. *Chapter 3* provides a more detailed discussion of the changes affecting medical devices and the more recent role of payers as gatekeepers, market access restrictions, and value metrics involved in evaluating medical devices.

It is evident from the timelines in *Figures 2.4* and *2.5* that many of the early examples of value assessment and payers acting as gatekeepers to market access are from outside the United States. Many industrialized countries have already addressed the need for value assessment within formalized processes. These figures also introduce a number of metrics used in value assessment, such as cost-effectiveness analysis (CEA) and meta-analysis.

## 2.3.2 ONGOING CHANGES IN THE U.S. MARKET

The United States has been slower to transition to payer-oriented systems to control health care budgets *(Figure 2.5)*. Today, however, we are in a period of incredible acceleration regarding the debate on health care funding and the creation of assessment and control systems. Given that the Canadian and U.S. markets accounted for approximately 40% of global pharmaceutical sales in 2009,[22] the changes in the U.S. system will have considerable ramifications for health care technology developers. Much of the U.S. activities, outlined in the box below, can be grouped into categories that reflect the foundation and evolution of the Value Era described in *Figure 2.3*.

**Figure 2.4 | Global (excluding the U.S.) timeline for the introduction of key public reimbursement bodies and advisory groups and new value assesment metrics.** [11,13,14,15,16,17,18,19,21,30,47]

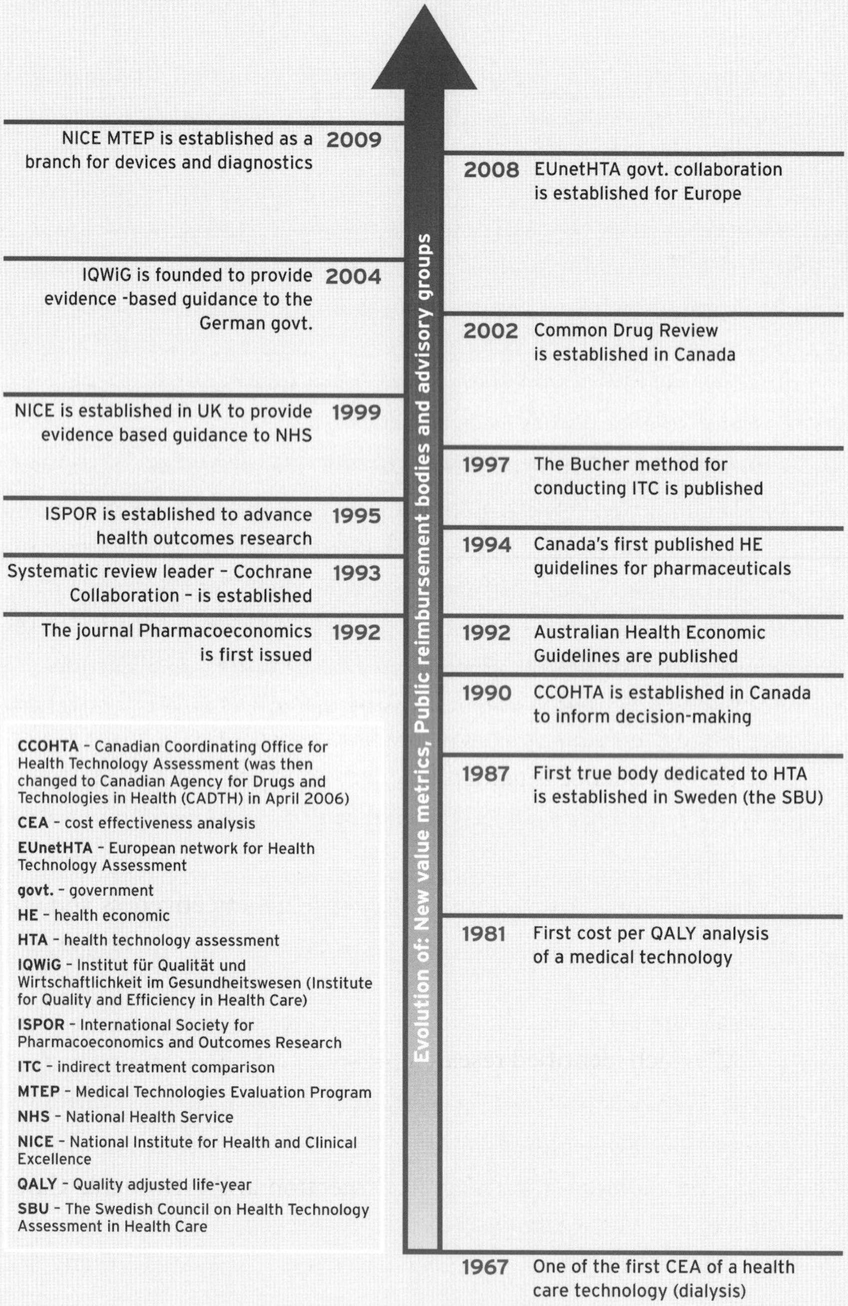

Evolution of: New value metrics, Public reimbursement bodies and advisory groups

NICE MTEP is established as a branch for devices and diagnostics — 2009

2008 — EUnetHTA govt. collaboration is established for Europe

IQWiG is founded to provide evidence -based guidance to the German govt. — 2004

2002 — Common Drug Review is established in Canada

NICE is established in UK to provide evidence based guidance to NHS — 1999

1997 — The Bucher method for conducting ITC is published

ISPOR is established to advance health outcomes research — 1995

1994 — Canada's first published HE guidelines for pharmaceuticals

Systematic review leader – Cochrane Collaboration – is established — 1993

The journal Pharmacoeconomics is first issued — 1992

1992 — Australian Health Economic Guidelines are published

1990 — CCOHTA is established in Canada to inform decision-making

1987 — First true body dedicated to HTA is established in Sweden (the SBU)

1981 — First cost per QALY analysis of a medical technology

1967 — One of the first CEA of a health care technology (dialysis)

**CCOHTA** – Canadian Coordinating Office for Health Technology Assessment (was then changed to Canadian Agency for Drugs and Technologies in Health (CADTH) in April 2006)

**CEA** – cost effectiveness analysis

**EUnetHTA** – European network for Health Technology Assessment

**govt.** – government

**HE** – health economic

**HTA** – health technology assessment

**IQWiG** – Institut für Qualität und Wirtschaftlichkeit im Gesundheitswesen (Institute for Quality and Efficiency in Health Care)

**ISPOR** – International Society for Pharmacoeconomics and Outcomes Research

**ITC** – indirect treatment comparison

**MTEP** – Medical Technologies Evaluation Program

**NHS** – National Health Service

**NICE** – National Institute for Health and Clinical Excellence

**QALY** – Quality adjusted life-year

**SBU** – The Swedish Council on Health Technology Assessment in Health Care

## Activities in the U.S. Market That Require Industry Adaptation

- Ongoing health care reform discussion and legislation.
- Payers as gatekeepers of health care spending.
- Increased use of cost containment activities, such as rebates, risk-sharing, and financial disincentives, as well as growing use of bundling, restrictive access, and limited-use criteria.
- Adoption of new evaluation metrics, such comparative effectiveness research (CER), CEA, HTA and budget impact.
- Creation of new technology assessment groups.

In the context of this book, some of the most relevant changes to the United States include the following:

- Coverage with Evidence Development (CED) recently instituted by the Medicare program, posits that evidence generated to support regulatory approval of a product is sometimes insufficient for coverage and reimbursement. It implies that evidence gaps may arise when trials supporting the product are considered to be of poor quality or because patient populations and settings are not representative of practice. The CED program is an attempt to permit reimbursement of the technology with the condition that additional evidence is gathered systematically (e.g., real-world prospective registries) to better understand risks and benefits relative to alternatives.[23,24]

- The concept of CER as a tool to improve the effectiveness and efficiency of health care emerged with reports from the Congressional Budget Office in 2007,[25] which examined options for expanded federal support for CER, and the Institute of Medicine (IOM) in 2009,[26] which identified research priorities for CER. Subsequent to these reports, $1.1 billion was allocated for CER within the American Recovery and Reinvestment Act (ARRA) in 2009.[27]

- The 2010 passing of the Patient Protection and Affordable Care Act (PPACA)[28] established a non-profit corporation known as the Patient-Centered Outcomes Research Institute (PCORI), to

**FIGURE 2.5 | U.S. timeline for the introduction of key budget control measures, advisory groups, and new value metrics.** [12,22,23,24,25,26,27,28,30,31,32,33,34,35,36,37,38,39,40,41]

| | |
|---|---|
| **2010** U.S. Health Care Reform initiated Patient Protection and Affordable Care Act | **2010** Establishment of Patient-Centred Outcomes Research Institute (PCORI) |
| **2008** WellPoint releases revised evidence requirements for pharmaceutical HTA | **2009** $1.1 billion allocated for CER by ARRA (NPAF launches CER database in 2011) |
| **2006** Coverage with evidence development (CED) (Medicare U.S.) | **2007** AMCP Guide to Pharmaceutical Payment incorporates rebating |
| **2004** U.S. health care spending is highest of all OECD countries (approx. 15% of GDP) | U.S. Congressional Budget Office (CBO) Report on Comparative Effectiveness |
| **1999** Marked increase in implementation of three-tier product coverage | **2000** AMCP's guidance on clinical and economic data for private payer formulary listings |
| | **1996** Gold et al. publish "Cost-Effectiveness in Health and Medicine" (US expert panel) |
| **1989** AHCPR is created under the Omnibus Budget Reconciliation Act (103.Stat.2159) | |
| | **1986** Start of John Hopkins Program for Medical Technology and Practice Assessment |
| | **1978** First cost benefit analysis published for an implantable medical device |
| | **1977** First publication on hospital purchasing committees |
| | **1976** The term "meta-analysis" was first coined by Gene Glass |
| | **1972** Office of Technology Assessment is established |

*Vertical axis labels: Metrics/guidelines, Budget control measures, Access restrictions by payers*

**AHCPR** - Agency for Health Care Policy and Research; later reauthorized with a name change as the Agency for Healthcare Research and Quality (AHRQ) in 1999 under the Healthcare Research and Quality Act of 1999
**AMCP** - Academy of Managed Care Pharmacy
**ARRA** - American Recovery and Reinvestment Act
**CEA** - cost-effectiveness analysis
**CER** - comparative effectiveness research
**GDP** - gross domestic product
**HTA** - health technology assessment
**NPAF** - The National Patient Advocate Foundation
**OECD** - Organisation for Economic Co-operation and Development
**OTA** - Office of Technology Assessment

"assist patients, clinicians, purchasers, and policymakers in making informed health decisions," through the conduct and dissemination of CER.[29]

## 2.3.3 THE IMPACT OF RESTRICTIONS TO MARKET ACCESS ON SALES

The increased role for payers changes the dynamic for commercialization of health care products. In this new environment, product awareness among clinicians no longer ensures product adoption. Instead, market access through payers and purchasers is required for product awareness and demand to translate into sales success. Restrictions may take many different forms of limited access as specified in *Table 2.2*. For hospital-based medical devices, the key hurdle is approval by hospital purchasing departments.

The creation of this new barrier to product success has changed the traditional relationship between price and demand *(Figure 2.6)*. In an unrestricted market, demand decreases as price increases for products *(Figure 2.6A)*. This simplified relationship can be applied to medical technologies where there are less expensive alternatives.

In restrictive markets, where payers control access, a different relationship exists *(Figure 2.6B)*. In these markets, it is assumed that a product has either unrestricted access or fully restricted access. Demand is insensitive to price as long as the product has full coverage by payers – that is, clinicians will be able to use the health care technology based on the needs of the patient. In this case, product awareness and clinical value drive demand. However, in a restrictive environment, a price will also exist where payers will withhold reimbursement. In this scenario, clinicians will be unable to use the technology, except in cases where the patient can fund the cost. As illustrated, in this restrictive environment there exists a threshold for price beyond which demand is substantially reduced. This extreme example reflects a number of real-world scenarios, such as NICE guidance in the UK, formulary inclusion in Canada and Australia, and purchasing decisions in U.S. hospitals.

**FIGURE 2.6 |** Relationship between product price and demand in cases of a market that is unrestricted (A), restricted (B), and progressively restricted (C).

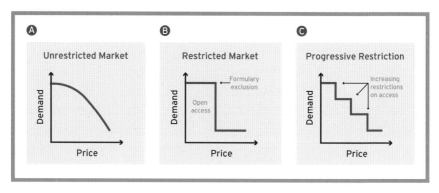

*Figure 2.6C* demonstrates another common scenario, where increasing price leads to increasing restrictions (such as co-payments), such that the maximum demand follows a stepped pattern. In all cases, traditional commercial activities are critical to maximizing the demand for and sales of a product, but the maximum for both is capped by restrictions placed by payers.

## 2.4 | The Metrics of the Value Era

Measuring value is subjective, as value means different things to different audiences *(Table 2.4)*. Traditionally, products have been defined and developed based on their value propositions for regulators, patients, and clinicians. These propositions have driven the metrics used to define product value and the data requirements for product development.

For example, regulators want safe, efficacious products and use statistically valid data from clinical trials as the metric for assessing value. In contrast, patients are most interested in feeling better without undue inconvenience or cost. The primary metrics for communicating value to patients are symptoms, functioning, and health-related quality of life (HRQOL).[f] Finally, physicians assess value through clinical trial data and other data on improvement of patients' signs, symptoms, and HRQOL. Thus, physicians' values overlap with regulators' and patients' values.

The pharmaceutical and medical device industries are well suited to generating the data relevant to communicating value to regulators, patients, and physicians. Trials are well designed to demonstrate clinical impact. HRQOL endpoints have been integrated into clinical trials and/or post-marketing research programs. Sales and marketing teams

**TABLE 2.4 | Defining value according to different stakeholders**

| | Value Components | Key Value Metrics |
|---|---|---|
| **Regulators** | • Safe<br>• Efficacious | • Clinical trial endpoints |
| **Patients** | • Improved health<br>• Convenient<br>• Affordable | • Symptoms and functioning<br>• Patient-reported outcomes (e.g., HRQOL)<br>• Out-of-pocket costs |
| **Physicians** | • Safe and effective<br>• Improved patient health<br>• Simple to administer/monitor | • Unmet clinical need<br>• Clinical data (e.g., clinical trials, meta-analyses, observational data)<br>• Clinician-assessed outcomes<br>• Patient-reported outcomes |
| **Payers** | • More effective and safer than comparable alternatives<br>• Better value for money<br>• Affordable | • Unmet clinical need<br>• Clinical data (e.g., clinical trials, meta-analyses, observational data)<br>• Patient-reported outcomes<br>• Health technology assessment<br>• Comparative effectiveness<br>• Cost-effectiveness<br>• Budget impact |

f   Health related quality of life (HRQOL) has emerged as a useful tool, as it captures in one measure all treatment impacts, including symptoms, side effects, and convenience. HRQOL is an outcome measure based on patents' perspectives of the impact of their condition and its treatment on their emotional, physical, and social functioning and lifestyle.[47] Measures that seek to determine physical health (e.g., fitness, symptoms, signs of disease and wellness), physical functioning (ability to perform daily activities and physical roles), social functioning, and social health (relationships, social support, and activities), psychological well-being (depression, anxiety), and emotional well-being (life satisfaction, morale, control, coping, and adjustment), and perceptions are considered HRQOL outcome measures. [47]

are experienced in communicating messages around these metrics to physician and patient audiences.

The emergence of payers as gatekeepers has created additional metrics for assessing product value. As discussed in the following section, these metrics are using methods from the HTA and health economics fields and require data that are beyond the traditional clinical trial and post-marketing research programs. As such, evidence generation must now extend beyond traditional research and development activities.

## 2.4.1 THE VOCABULARY OF VALUE ASSESSMENT METRICS

The most important element that is repeated throughout this section defining the terms of value assessment is the comparative nature of value from the viewpoint of payers. Payers make budget allocation decisions; as such, they must decide between products. This involves selecting products for funding from among a therapeutic class or, more commonly, selecting products from among all the possible treatment options for a given condition. For example, when making funding decisions for obesity management, payers need to consider surgical (gastric bypass), pharmaceutical (e.g., appetite suppressants), and device (gastric banding) options.

The need for comparative analysis is reflected in the tools of HTA and the very name of CER. These types of comparative analyses often require consideration of data beyond individual clinical trials. Instead, the analyses combine data from multiple trials, using such techniques as indirect treatment comparisons (ITCs), meta-analysis, and disease simulation models. The interventions of interest will extend beyond the comparators in a product's randomized controlled trials (RCTs). CER will also extend beyond the populations in a product's RCTs to include subgroups of patients defined by age, co-morbidities, or genetic characteristics.

The following definitions are provided for several important value metrics used throughout this book.

## Health Technology Assessment

HTA is a dynamic, rapidly evolving process that informs real-world decisions, such as reimbursement policy, about the value (e.g., benefits, risks, costs) of new and existing health care technologies.[42] HTA plays an integral role in evidence-based decision making. Without good evidence, a technology update may be influenced by a range of social, financial, and institutional factors that may result in suboptimal health outcomes and inefficient use of resources.[38] As such, HTAs are important for improving the efficiency of health care systems and determining where health care resources should be best allocated. Sample questions that HTA may consider follow, although scope, methods, and practice will vary by region:

- Is the new technology safe and clinically effective?
- How does the technology compare with existing alternatives or standards of care?
- In which population(s) does the technology work?
- What is the cost impact of the technology?

To answer these questions, several of the value metrics described in this section are encompassed within a typical HTA. HTA focuses on the collective analysis of data using systematic reviews, meta-analyses, and possibly ITCs or network meta-analyses. In this regard, HTA is similar to CER, as they both focus on comparative analyses of interventions to assess relative clinical value. However, HTA often also includes the consideration of costs, with value metrics such as CEA being applicable.

## Comparative Effectiveness Research

The IOM has defined CER as "the generation and synthesis of evidence that compares the benefits and harms of alternative methods to prevent, diagnose, treat, and monitor a clinical condition, or to improve the delivery of care. The purpose of CER is to assist consumers, clinicians, purchasers, and policy makers to make informed decisions that will improve healthcare at both the individual and population levels."[43]

The methods of CER will evolve over the coming years. It is expected that CER will borrow from HTA methodology, with the use of systematic reviews, meta-analyses, and ITCs – all of which reflect evidence "synthesis." However, CER is expected to extend beyond HTA in the area of evidence "generation" through use of prospective, pragmatic (or naturalistic) trials. These CER clinical research trials measure effectiveness;[g] they differ from other clinical trials, which more narrowly measure efficacy.[h] Pragmatic trial designs seek to address the limited external validity of clinical trials conducted under strict protocol specifications in restricted patient subsets, by including comparators that reflect current care, patients with common co-morbid conditions, diverse demographic characteristics, and a broad range of providers. The possibility that prospective CER will be required from the industry or conducted independently represents one of the greatest uncertainties and largest possible impacts for the industry. A requirement for additional pragmatic RCTs represents a substantial financial cost to the industry or to public funders. In addition, this requirement may impact the adoption of effective new therapies due to the time required for such studies.

Government-funded CER within the PPACA framework is expected to exclude economic analysis. However, there is continuing debate as to whether CER should include economic evaluations, such as CEA. Nevertheless, whether CEA is included within CER may be irrelevant. Given the rich history of CEA in many jurisdictions and the obvious budget implications of adopting new health care technologies, it is likely that payers will seek or conduct CEA data to supplement CER findings.

### Meta-analysis

Originally defined as "the analysis of analyses," meta-analysis was first coined by Gene Glass in his 1976 presidential address to the American Educational Research Association.[12,44] Meta-analyses, which

---

[g] **Effectiveness:** the treatment benefit produced in routine or "usual" clinical practice.
[h] **Efficacy:** the treatment benefit produced under ideal experimental conditions, typically a clinical trial setting.

are completed by the quantitative statistical pooling of results from independent but combinable studies, are widely used in epidemiology and evidence-based medicine today.[44] In the 1980s, meta-analyses became increasingly popular in medicine. In 1993, the Cochrane Collaboration was established[16] – a group that facilitated the conduct of meta-analyses in all areas of health care.

Essentially, the meta-analytic approach may be used to overcome the problem of insufficient sample size and resultant inconclusive evidence. Meta-analyses are traditionally conducted by combining results of RCTs that compare two or more therapies; however, they may also be conducted with nonrandomized, observational studies. A meta-analysis should minimize bias by including high-quality, comparable studies. Finally, meta-analyses are often – but not always – important components of a systematic review.

### Systematic Reviews

These literature reviews focus on a research question that tries to identify, appraise, select, and synthesize all high-quality research evidence relevant to that question. A systematic review has a qualitative, literature description component and often – but not always – incorporates a quantitative meta-analytical component.

### Indirect Treatment Comparison

In ideal scenarios, clinical trials are available that directly compare relevant products. However, in most cases the trials could not possibly include all relevant treatment alternatives without jeopardizing the regulatory objectives of the trial. ITCs allow the comparison of an intervention to other interventions not studied in the clinical trial. They are increasingly being used globally (e.g., HTA organizations) to address important research questions and inform decision making within the constraints of the available data.[42] In contrast to direct within-trial comparisons, an ITC refers to a between-study comparison of different interventions.

As a simplified example, suppose one trial compares therapy A to B, and another compares therapy B to C. An ITC of therapy A versus C can be conducted based on the relative effects of each therapy versus B.[45] As the number of comparators and trials increases, so does the complexity of conducting such analyses, and more sophisticated methodologies (i.e., multiple treatment comparisons [MTCs]) are used.[45] ITCs and MTCs (both sometimes referred to as network meta-analyses) are increasingly being conducted for both drug therapies and medical devices.

### Patient-Reported Outcomes (PROs)

This umbrella term covers a range of potential measurements, but focuses on the consequences of disease and/or its treatment as reported by the patient (e.g., perceptions of health, well-being, symptom experience, functioning, and treatment satisfaction).[46] PRO data may be collected via questionnaires completed by the patient or via interviews.[46] PROs have moved into mainstream clinical research over the past decade, with the acceptance by regulatory agencies of PRO endpoints in labeling claims. The most commonly used PRO questionnaires may assess the following factors:[47]

- Global impression
- Symptoms (impairments)
- Functional status (disability)
- Well-being
- HRQOL
- Satisfaction with treatment
- Treatment adherence
- Utility/preference-based measures

### Health Economics

This discipline deals with the application of economic principles and theories to health and the health sector. Driven by scarcity, health economics is based on the fact that health care resources are limited and choices have to be made regarding their use. To optimize health with the given resources available, efficiency[i] must be maximized, a concept often referred to by health economists as the "third step of evidence" after efficacy and effectiveness.[48] For health care interventions, this involves assessing whether they provide good value for money and are, therefore, an efficient use of limited resources. Many of the value metrics described in this section (e.g., CEA, ITC, models) may be used within a health economics study.

## Cost-Effectiveness analysis

Health economics guidelines for formulary submissions began in Australia in the early 1990s and quickly spread to Canada and Europe. Although health economics is a broad field of research, its primary focus is cost-effectiveness analysis, which is also known as economic evaluation, or pharmaco-economics when applied to pharmaceutical products. CEAs are an increasingly important tool in comparing the relative efficacy and cost of alternative health care interventions. Since organizations that fund health care cannot fund every intervention due to budgetary constraints and economic pressures, efficiency is one of their major priorities – i.e., support interventions that provide the greatest value for the money invested. CEAs compare the relative expenditures (costs) and outcomes (effects) of two or more courses of action. Alternatively, a cost-utility analysis seeks to standardize the health effects into a quality-adjusted life year (QALY).[i,49]

CEAs are most commonly performed using decision analytic modeling.[50] The data used are based mostly on results from RCTs and observational cohorts. The result of a CEA is displayed as an

---

i   **Efficiency:** In health care, efficiency refers to when money spent on an intervention is money spent well. In other words, if it were possible to achieve greater health gains in any area of health with the same money by spending it on something else, the intervention examined is relatively inefficient.[48] The crucial metric is the ratio between the cost needed to carry out the intervention and its health effects, often referred to as the cost-effectiveness ratio.

i   **Quality-adjusted life year (QALY):** is a parameter that combines the quality and quantity of a person's life. A QALY takes into consideration life expectancy and the quality of remaining years, to allow a relative comparison between a variety of treatments and disease states. For example, two products may extend life by 10 years, one with patients in good health and the other with patients in a coma. The first therapy would produce more QALYs, as the quality of life in good health is higher than in a coma. Therefore, the values represent "quality-weighted" health states and reflect the desirability of living in a particular state. A higher weight reflects a better or more preferred state (i.e., where perfect health corresponds to 1, suboptimal health would be <1, death corresponds to 0, and in some cases a negative value would be considered worse than death).

incremental cost-effectiveness ratio (ICER), which is a measure of the incremental cost associated with gaining one unit of health. Plotting the ICER (incremental cost versus incremental clinical effect) on a cost-effectiveness plane allows intuitive visualization of a CEA's results. *Figure 2.7A* illustrates this relationship to a sample threshold for decision making in *Figure 2.7B*. Since most new treatments that show increased efficacy are associated with a higher cost, the ICER provides a measure to determine cost-effectiveness. For many jurisdictions, evidence of cost-effectiveness has become mandatory for reimbursement of treatment.

**Cost-Effectiveness Model (CEM)**

This mathematical framework for the conduct of CEAs is meant to simulate a clinical condition (e.g., osteoporosis) or a clinical decision (e.g., methods for diagnosing disease). A CEM is often required for a CEA, as the decision being considered requires data that are beyond any given RCT. As such, the analysis requires combination of data from several sources (e.g., multiple trials, epidemiology data, resource costs) in order to fully explore the cost-effectiveness of a given intervention compared to other available options.

The most commonly used types of CEMs are: (1) decision analytic models, which use a decision tree to describe choices for care (e.g., diagnostic test A versus diagnostic test B) and the probability of downstream events (e.g., false positive, false negative), based on those choices; and (2) Markov models (also called state transition models), which commonly describes a health condition (e.g., osteoporosis) as a series of mutually exclusive health states (e.g., well, acute fracture, post-fracture, dead), between which patients may transition based on population probabilities and treatment effect. Other less common model types are discrete event simulations and individual patient simulations.

**Thresholds for Cost-Effectiveness**

A cost-effectiveness threshold refers to the maximum ICER that is associated with a high probability of reimbursement for an intervention. Strict criteria on acceptable thresholds for the cost-effectiveness

**FIGURE 2.7** | Relationship between the incremental cost and incremental clinical effect for a treatment. Part (A) illustrates the four quadrants for possible cost-effectiveness results defined by cost and treatment effect of an intervention compared to a standard of care. Part (B) demonstrates an incremental cost-effectiveness ratio (ICER) from a CEA in relation to a threshold for maximum cost effectiveness.

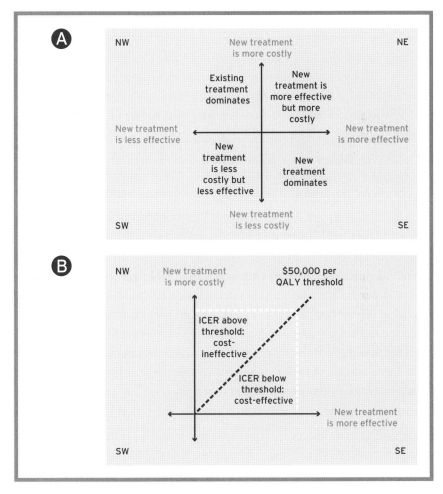

of a health care product do not exist in any jurisdiction. Instead, payers and other decisions makers reserve the right to decide on whether a product is cost-effective based on factors that include (but are not limited to) the ICER (e.g., cost per QALY gained ratio). However, general trends have been observed and discussed in the literature.

Economic advisors to NICE have suggested that interventions with an ICER of less than £20,000 per QALY gained should be considered cost-effective, and therapies above £30,000 per QALY gained should be considered cost-effective only in certain circumstances. A study by Devlin and Parkin (2004)[51] found that product reimbursement varies by factors, such as the unmet clinical need, the severity of the condition, and the affordability of adoption. It documented rejections of products with ratios as low as £19,000 per QALY and acceptances of products with ratios up to £46,000 per QALY.

Thresholds in other countries are less transparent, though Canadian payers are unlikely to reimburse therapies for chronic conditions with low associated mortality if the ratio is above $20,000 CDN per QALY. However, ratios of up to $75,000 CDN per QALY may be acceptable for therapies treating conditions with high mortality, such as cancer. In the United States, the threshold for reimbursement decisions is unclear, as formal processes for consideration of cost-effectiveness within reimbursement decisions do not exist for any public or private payers. However, it has been noted that the threshold for policy decision making is likely to be between $50,000 and $100,000 USD,[52] depending on the particular treatment and other factors.

## Budget Impact Analysis (BIA)

Often omitted from the broader discussion of health economics and economic evaluation, BIAs are less readily available in the published literature. However, a BIA is a critical component for payers/purchasers and can play a pivotal role in the decisions regarding a product's market access. At a minimum, a BIA includes the impact of the introduction of the new product on the purchaser's budget. The analysis will include the new product's projected market share and the products it is expected to replace. This information is typically combined with estimates of the product's market size and unit costs, to provide a projection of its budget impact over a specified time period (e.g., three years).

BIAs may also consider cost offsets from other areas of spending, such as the cost savings from a new product's reduction in the length of hospitalization and other improved resource efficiencies. The inclusion of offsetting costs for other areas of spending will depend on the requirement of local payers, with many payers excluding such data.

### Value-Based Pricing (VBP)

This method often determines price thresholds for a given product based on CEA. The price threshold represents the point where the ICER threshold would be reached and possible restrictions in market access would occur. VBP is based on the theory that pricing should reflect a product's value, as payers will evaluate a product's impact on market success.[53] The common methodology for VBP is a CEA based on a disease simulation model, where the impact of a therapy on clinical outcomes and disease costs can be estimated compared to existing standards of care.

## REFERENCES

1   Organisation for Economic Co-operation and Development. Social expenditure: Aggregated data, OECD Social Expenditure Statistics (database). 2011.
2   Collier R. Rapidly rising clinical trial costs worry researchers. *CMAJ* 2009; 180:277-8.
3   U.S. Department of Commerce Economics and Statistics Administration. U.S. Census Bureau: Demographic trends in the 20th century. Census. 2000 Special Reports. 2002.
4   Alemayehu B, et al. The lifetime distribution of health care costs. *Health Serv Res* 2004; 39:627-42.
5   Hong KW, et al. Overview of personalized medicine in the disease genomic era. *BMB Rep* 2010; 43:643-8.
6   Time Magazine. Archive: Search results from Jan 1, 1967, to Dec 31, 2004. Available at: http://search.time.com/results.html?N=45&Ns=p_date_range|1&Ntt=&Nf=p_date_range%7cBTWN+19670101+20041231. [Accessed on: March 13, 2012]
7   Rosenheck RA, et al. Developing a policy for second-generation antipsychotic drugs. *Health Aff* (Millwood) 2009; 28:782-93.
8   Van Herck P, et al. Systematic review: Effects, design choices, and context of pay-for-performance in health care. *BMC Health Serv Res* 2010; 10:247.
9   Carlson JJ, et al. Linking payment to health outcomes: A taxonomy and examination of performance-based reimbursement schemes between healthcare payers and manufacturers. *Health Policy* 2010; 96:179-90.
10  Drummond MF, et al. Key principles for the improved conduct of health technology assessments for resource allocation decisions. *Int J Technol Assess Health Care* 2008; 24: 244-58; discussion 362-8.
11  Velasco-Garrido M, et al. Health technology assessment: An introduction to objectives, role of evidence, and structure in Europe. Policy Brief, World Health Organization 2005 on behalf of the European Observatory on Health Systems and Policies, 2005.

[12] Rosenthal R, et al. Meta-analysis: Recent developments in quantitative methods for literature reviews. *Annu Rev Psychol* 2001; 52:59-82.

[13] The Canadian Agency for Drugs and Technologies in Health. History. Available at: http://www.cadth.ca/en/cadth/history. [Accessed on: March 13, 2012]

[14] Australian Government. Department of Health and Ageing. Guidelines for the pharmaceutical industry. Part 4 About these guidelines. Available at: http://www.health.gov.au/internet/main/publishing.nsf/content/health-pbs-general-pubs-guidelines-part4.htm. [Accessed on: March 13, 2012]

[15] Bucher HC, et al. The results of direct and indirect treatment comparisons in meta-analysis of randomized controlled trials. *J Clin Epidemiol* 1997; 50:683-91

[16] The Cochrane Collaboration. About us. Available at: http://www.cochrane.org/about-us. [Accessed on: March 13, 2012]

[17] Institute for Quality and Efficiency in Health Care. Responsibilities and objectives of IQWiG. Available at: https://www.iqwig.de/responsibilities-objectives.932.en.html?random=546ca8. [Accessed on: March 13, 2012]

[18] National Institute for Health and Clinical Excellence. NICE Medical Technologies Evaluation Programme welcomes new external assessment centre. Available at: http://www.nice.org.uk/newsroom/pressreleases/MTEPWelcomesNewEAC.jsp. [Accessed on: March 13, 2012]

[19] European network for Health Technology Assessment. About. Available at: http://www.eunethta.eu/Public/About_EUnetHTA/. [Accessed on: March 13, 2012]

[20] Bootman JL, Rowland C, Wertheimer AI: Cost-benefit analysis: a research tool for evaluating innovative health programs. *Eval Health Prof* 1979; 2:129-54.

[21] Pliskin JS, Stason WB, Weinstein MC, et al: Coronary artery bypass graft surgery: clinical decision making and cost-effectiveness analysis. *Med Decis Making* 1981; 1:10-28.

[22] European Federation of Pharmaceutical Industries and Associations. The pharmaceutical industry in figures. 2010 edition: Belgium. Available at: http://www.bioin.or.kr/upload/industry/1281397427349.pdf [Accessed on: March 13, 2012]

[23] Centers for Medicare & Medicaid Services (CMS): Coverage with evidence development. Available at: https://www.cms.gov/CoverageGenInfo/03_CED.asp. [Accessed on: March 13, 2012]

[24] Centers for Medicare & Medicaid Services. Guidance for the public, industry, and CMS staff: National coverage determinations with data collection as a condition of coverage: Coverage with evidence development. 2006.

[25] Congressional Budget Office. Research on the comaprative effectiveness of medical treatments. 2007.

[26] Institute of Medicine of the National Academies. Initial national priorities for comparative effectiveness research. Washington, DC, The National Academies Press, 2009.

[27] NPAF. National Patient Advocate Foundation launches comparative effectiveness research (CER) database. January 6, 2011.

[28] Senate and House of Representatives of the United States of America in Congress. Patient Protection and Affordable Care Act of 2010. January 5, 2010.

[29] Patient-Centered Outcomes Research Institute. Mission statement. Available at: http://www.pcori.org/about/mission/. [Accessed on: March 13, 2012]

[30] Smith WF. Cost-effectiveness and cost-benefit analyses for public health programs. *Public Health Rep* 1968; 83:899-906.

[31] Motheral B, et al. Effect of a three-tier prescription copay on pharmaceutical and other medical utilization. *Med Care* 2001; 39:1293-304.

[32] Gold MS, et al. Cost-effectiveness in health and medicine. New York, NY, Oxford University Press, 1997.

[33] Academy of Managed Care Pharmacy. AMCP guide to pharmaceutical payment methods: Exclusive edition. 2007.

[34] Cornell University ILR School. U.S. health care spending: Comparison with other OECD countries. 2007.

[35] Sullivan SD, et al. Health technology assessment in health-care decisions in the United States. *Value Health* 2009; 12 Suppl 2:S39-44.

[36] Patient-Centered Outcomes Research Institute. About us. Available at: http://www.pcori.org/about. [Accessed on: March 13, 2012]

[37] Cooalition Working Group. Principles of a Sound Drug Formulary System. 2000. Available at: http://www.amcp.org/WorkArea/DownloadAsset.aspx?id=9280 [Accessed on: March 13, 2012]

38 Sorenson C, et al. Applying health economics for policy decision making: Do devices differ from drugs? *Europace* 2011; 13 Suppl 2:ii54-8.

39 Boergadine L. Committees ensure cost efficiency in purchasing. *Hospitals* 1977; 51:133-5.

40 Fabricius J. A cost benefit analysis of different types of pacemaker. Scand J *Thorac Cardiovasc Surg* 1978; Suppl:35-7.

41 Steinberg EP, Graziano S: Integrating technology assessment and medical practice evaluation into hospital operations. *QRB Qual Rev Bull* 1990; 16:218-22.

42 Drummond MF, et al. Key principles for the improved conduct of health technology assessments for resource allocation decisions. *Int J Technol Assess Health Care* 2008; 24:244-58; discussion 362-8.

43 Committee on Comparative Effectiveness Research Prioritization: Board on Health Care Services (HCS): Institute of Medicine of the National Academies. Initial national priorities for comparative effectiveness research 2009.

44 Egger M, et al. Where now for meta-analysis? *Int J Epidemiol* 2002; 31:1-5.

45 Jansen JP, et al. Interpreting indirect treatment comparisons and network meta-analysis for health-care decision making: Report of the ISPOR Task Force on Indirect Treatment Comparisons Good Research Practices: Part 1. *Value Health* 2011; 14:417-28.

46 Coons SJ, et al. Recommendations on evidence needed to support measurement equivalence between electronic and paper-based patient-reported outcome (PRO) measures: ISPOR ePRO Good Research Practices Task Force report. *Value Health* 2009; 12:419-29.

47 International Society for Pharmacoeconomics and Outcomes Research. Patient-reported outcomes (PRO). Available at: http://www.ispor.org/terminology/default.asp. [Accessed on: March 13, 2012]

48 Annemans L. Health economics for non-economists. An introduction to the concepts, methods and pitfalls of health economic evaluation. The Netherlands,Gent. Academia Press, 2008.

49 Neumann PJ, et al. Are methods for estimating QALYs in cost-effectiveness analyses improving? *Med Decis Making* 1997; 17:402-8.

50 O'Brien B. Economic evaluation of pharmaceuticals. Frankenstein's monster or vampire of trials? *Med Care* 34:DS99-108, 1996.

51 Devlin N, et al. Does NICE have a cost-effectiveness threshold and what other factors influence its decisions? A binary choice analysis. *Health Econ* 2004; 13:437-52.

52 Grosse SD, et al. Lessons from cost-effectiveness research for United States public health policy. *Annu Rev Public Health* 2007; 28:365-91.

53 The Henry J. Kaiser Family Foundation. Health Reform Source. Implementation timeline: Medicare value-based purchasing. Available at: http://healthreform.kff.org/timeline.aspx?source=QL. [Accessed on: March 13, 2012]

# CHAPTER 3

# The Value Era and Medical Devices

## KEY MESSAGE:

The current medical device landscape is characterized by a changed customer base whereby decision-making power is shifting from physicians to become more collaborative and include hospital purchasers. The drivers of the Value Era, payers as gatekeepers, market access restrictions, and new value metrics, have become very relevant for medical device manufacturers who must keenly acknowledge these concepts in developing successful market access strategies.

## CONCEPTS DISCUSSED:

- Principles of product adoption and product awareness applied to medical devices.
- Evolving and expanded customer base for medical devices.
- New decision-making processes, such as hospital technology assessment committees.

The medical device landscape is currently experiencing several challenges. While awareness of a product's existence, availability, and value through traditional commercial activities is anticipated to remain critical to its success, new steps will be required to ensure product adoption in today's medical device market. Understanding the changing processes and new requirements is essential to building an integrated strategy for achieving success in this new marketplace. Several of these changes are applicable to developed regions, such as North America, Europe, and Australia; however, this chapter focuses on U.S. examples, given the ongoing and rapid changes in the U.S. market. In particular, several references are made to the U.S. Centers for Medicare & Medicaid Services (CMS), as it is the largest public payer in the world.

## 3.1 | Medical Devices and Their Roles in Health Care Systems

While the challenges noted in this chapter apply to all medical devices, processes and requirements will vary by type of device. This chapter provides several examples, with a focus on implantable devices associated with inpatient care. Such implantable devices have been reported to comprise up to 55% of total hospital supply expenses.[1] *Table 3.1* defines a medical device and its subsets.

Medical devices follow a unique pathway within the health care system. *Figure 3.1* describes a simplification of this pathway. Essentially, once a medical device is approved for use, it can be purchased. Hospitals and health care facilities are the primary purchasers of medical devices. Payers (e.g., national governments) often ultimately reimburse[k] hospitals based on specific coding,[l] coverage,[m] and payment[n]

---

[k] **Reimbursement:** is a term describing how payers pay for the items or services provided by medical professionals. Reimbursement can be broken down into three components: coverage, coding, and payment.

[l] **Coding:** Alpha-numeric systems (e.g., ICD-9, CPT) that typically describe medical services, procedures, and diagnoses, which are often required for insurance purposes and involved in payment processes.

[m] **Coverage:** Payers determine whether, and to what extent, they will pay for services, procedures, and products.

[n] **Payment:** If the coverage decision is positive, the payer determines how much to reimburse hospitals based on several elements (e.g., average diagnosis-related group costs).

**TABLE 3.1 | Definitions of medical device and its subsets**

| | |
|---|---|
| **Medical Device**[2] | • Any instrument, apparatus, appliance, software, material or other article, whether used alone or in combination, together with any accessories, intended by the manufacturer to be used for humans for diagnosis, prevention, monitoring, treatment or alleviation of a disease/injury (also includes conception control). |
| | • A medical device also does not achieve its principal intended action within the human body by pharmacological, immunological or metabolic means but may be assisted in its function by such means. |
| **Subsets of Medical Devices** | |
| **Active Medical Device**[3] | • Any medical device relying for its' functioning on a source of electrical energy or any source of power other than directly generated by the human body or gravity (e.g., harmonic scalpel). |
| **Implantable Medical Device**[3] | • Any medical device that is intended both (1) to be totally or partly introduced, surgically or medically, into the human body or by medical intervention into a natural orifice, and (2) to remain after the procedure (e.g., stents, stent grafts, and implantable defibrillators). |
| **In vitro Diagnostic Medical Device**[4] | • Any medical device that is a reagent, reagent product, calibrator, control material, kit, instrument, apparatus, equipment or system used in vitro for examination of specimens (e.g., blood, tissue) for providing information concerning a physiological or pathological state, congenital abnormality, safety/compatibility with potential recipients, or for monitoring therapeutic measures (e.g., cervical pap test screening systems). |

processes. In many countries, reimbursement for devices is often based on the average procedure/diagnosis cost, rather than the specific device. However, in some cases, the payer may have additional payment codes for the use of specific devices. Physicians implant or utilize the device, and patients are the ultimate recipients.

For example, percutaneous coronary interventions (PCIs) utilize a range of medical devices (drug-eluting stents (DES), bare-metal stents (BMS), catheters, closure devices, etc.). To pay for PCIs, hospitals may receive a global budget from payers, based on historical hospital spending, which they must allocate to different procedures, including PCI (e.g., Canada[5]). Hospitals may also receive reimbursement specific to the PCI procedure, which incorporates the average cost of devices used (e.g., United States[6]). Finally, hospitals may receive separate supplementary reimbursement for certain devices (e.g., France).[7]

**FIGURE 3.1 |** Pathway for funding and using medical devices in health care

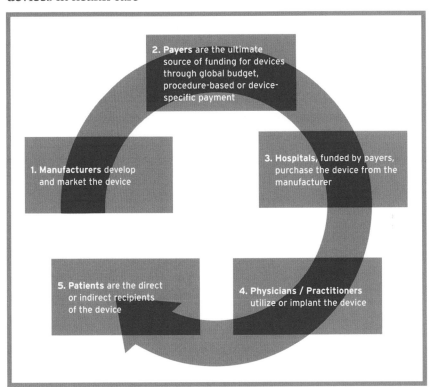

## 3.2 | Past Process for Obtaining Market Access for Medical Devices

For several decades, the health technology industry generated success by marketing safe and effective products to physicians who would create product demand for them and spur their adoption. For medical devices in particular, physician demand translated almost directly into product adoption by finance and materials management personnel at hospitals.[8,9,10] Medical device companies traditionally relied on close relationships with physicians to both sell and enhance their products. When hospital resources were available, physicians' requests were more influential than product purchase price in decisions for acquiring medical devices.[11] It has been reported that if price were questioned, the typical response of a sales representative would be to cover the important clinical features of the technology, have a physician recommend its purchase, and offer several contracting options.[12]

As such, physicians were viewed as the predominant medical device customer in the past *(Figure 3.2)*. Physicians were the primary users of medical device products as part of diagnostic or therapeutic interventions and needed to understand the device profile and be trained in its use. Physicians tended to use devices developed by one particular manufacturer, often due to having trained in a hospital that used that manufacturer's products or to past experience, and were reluctant to switch.[13]

Prior to the recent health care crisis, hospitals typically had ample budgets and fairly unrestricted reimbursement through payers. Thus, they were less likely to restrict device choice due to costs. Economic factors, and thus economic decision makers such as payers and hospital purchasers, played less of a role. Instead, key factors for evaluating devices included efficacy and safety, and physicians were the most appropriate evaluators of products for these criteria. An additional factor – most relevant perhaps from a U.S. perspective – is that many physicians had their own practices, which meant that they could send patients to hospitals of their choice. Such referrals were a privilege for hospitals due to the revenue they generated, providing another important reason why physicians had substantial influence over product selection at hospitals.[14]

The solutions used to achieve hospital product adoption were contingent on the role of the physician as the primary customer. Typically, product awareness activities *(Figure 3.3)* were aimed at increasing the likelihood that physicians and other influencers recognized a product's existence, availability, and value. Such activities often included training physicians for a device's use, education regarding a product's profile, conferences and publications, physician advisory boards, key opinion leader discussions to inform a device's development, and establishment of product loyalty with physicians. These activities were

**FIGURE 3.2 | Factors influencing the physician as the former primary customer for medical devices**

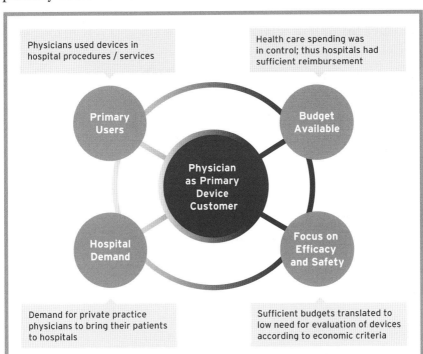

Physicians used devices in hospital procedures / services

Health care spending was in control; thus hospitals had sufficient reimbursement

Primary Users

Budget Available

Physician as Primary Device Customer

Hospital Demand

Focus on Efficacy and Safety

Demand for private practice physicians to bring their patients to hospitals

Sufficient budgets translated to low need for evaluation of devices according to economic criteria

further aimed at increasing the chances that physicians would prefer the product by helping to increase their comfort level with its use and their knowledge of its features and benefits, as well as their involvement with developing the evidence base.

Given the nature of these product awareness efforts, as well as physicians' influence on decision making, it is evident why such activities typically led to product adoption. As shown in *Figure 3.3*, the concepts of product awareness and product adoption fell under a single entity, where a common set of marketing activities typically led to successful market access. The figure illustrates that physicians interacted with hospitals, patients, and payer stakeholders to share knowledge, but they were the focal point of industry sales and marketing activities.

**FIGURE 3.3 |** Past market access process for medical devices, illustrating (1) physicians as the primary customer and influencer of product adoption, and (2) product awareness activities leading to product adoption.

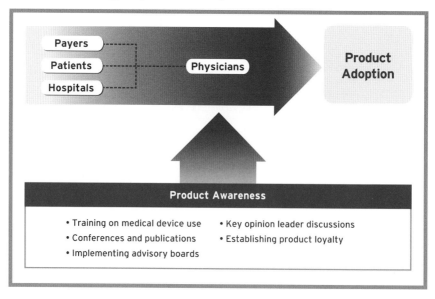

## 3.3 | Current Process and Requirements for Obtaining Market Access

The medical device landscape is undergoing rapid and continuous transformation, as governments around the world implement efforts to control health care costs. As a result of budget reductions and cost containment initiatives, the requirements for coverage and reimbursement have expanded in several regions, such as the United States and Europe. For medical device companies, the convergence of these challenges has ultimately created a new marketplace characterized by changed customers with new needs.

## Characteristics of the Changed Medical Device Landscape

- Changed Customer Base: Hospital decision makers, public and private payers, and sometimes patients are increasingly becoming more important in terms of decisions affecting medical device adoption.
- New Processes: New processes and groups, such as hospital technology assessment committees, are emerging. This trend has resulted in expanded evaluation of medical device evidence prior to adoption.
- New Data Needs: Requirements by both payers and hospital decision makers are expanding from traditional regulatory requirements (e.g., efficacy and safety) to evidence that supports the entire value proposition of a product, including both clinical and economic value compared to relevant alternative treatments.

In the past, well-executed product awareness activities targeting physicians resulted in significant product adoption. In today's environment, such activities no longer ensure product adoption because they do not fulfill all of the needs of today's relevant customers. *Figure 3.4* provides an overview of how different customers and new activities are now involved in decisions affecting the adoption of medical devices.

As cost containment pressures have increased, pricing and reimbursement have become more challenging. Similar to the pharmaceutical industry, payers have become important gatekeepers for access to medical devices and critical customers for the industry. In addition, hospitals (i.e., materials management, finance/purchasing departments) have emerged as a second hurdle for medical devices, as they may restrict access to a device or more forcefully negotiate its purchase. This evolution has complicated the landscape for activities promoting medical devices.

A recent survey of medical device and diagnostic company executives across North America, Europe, and Asia-Pacific showed that more than 40% of executives no longer view physicians as the primary customer; rather, other customers are becoming increasingly more important – a trend that is expected to increase.[9] *Figure 3.5* provides an overview of key factors involved in inclusively viewing payers, hospitals, physicians, and patients as important customers in today's medical device landscape.

**FIGURE 3.4 | The current process for gaining market access to medical devices, illustrating the continued need for product awareness efforts and the new requirement for value demonstration activities that are mainly targeted toward payers and hospital purchasers.**

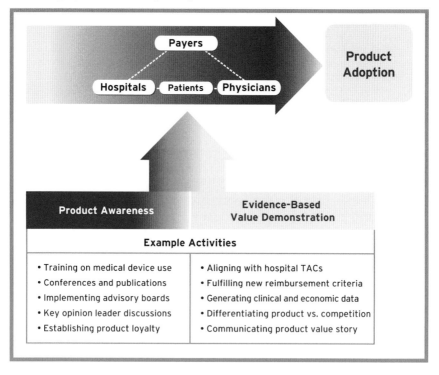

**FIGURE 3.5 |** Key factors involved in viewing payers, hospitals, physicians and patients as important customers in today's medical device landscape.

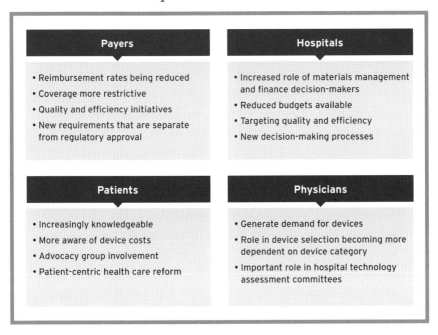

### 3.3.1 NEW PROCESSES AND REQUIREMENTS FOR PAYERS

**Summary of New Processes and Requirements for Payers**

- Regarding devices, payers generally have two methods of influence to control costs and improve quality of care: (1) Restricting coverage (e.g., coverage may be approved for limited patients) and (2) Setting payment rates (e.g., reimbursement amount may not always cover device costs).
- Requirements for payer reimbursement have expanded beyond traditional efficacy and safety data to include value metrics such as health technology assessment (HTA), comparative effectiveness research (CER), cost-effectiveness analysis (CEA), and budget impact analysis (BIA).

Similar to the discussion in the previous chapter, both public and private payers are now critical to the market success of medical devices. In fact, the availability of payer reimbursement, in addition to proven effectiveness, has been identified as the single largest factor in having hospitals purchase new medical technology today.[15] Generally, payers have two methods of influence:

- **Restricting coverage:** Payers can restrict access to a new device (or procedure involving the device) by not providing coverage. A recent U.S. study reported that coverage of technologies has become more restrictive, with CMS estimated to be 10 times less likely to cover technologies in 2006 compared to the early 2000s, particularly if evidence were limited.[16] In addition, payers may restrict coverage to smaller sub-populations, or with certain criteria, as a mechanism to control costs and reduce safety risks.

- **Setting payment rates:** Payers often set the reimbursement amount/payment for the procedures or services that require implantable (e.g., artificial joints or vascular stents) or non-implantable (e.g., tissue ablation devices, scalpels, laparoscopic tools) devices. Payers can limit the use of more expensive devices for a given procedure by failing to offer increased payment according to actual costs. For instance, in the United States in the 1990s, the list price of premium-coated hip constructs was less than half of the reimbursement amount for a hip replacement procedure.[17] However, the cost of these devices is currently outpacing the procedure reimbursement amount and therefore challenging hospital budgets.[17] Although for most countries additional payments can be made to hospitals to cover the costs of certain high-priced devices that represent technological advances, a significant lag time can exist before payment rates reflect new costs.[12]

As part of the new decision-making processes, payers have expanded evidence requirements and methods for assessing a product's value, which are above and beyond those needed for regulatory approval. In the United States for example, in addition to efficacy and safety, Medicare criteria for evaluating the coverage potential of technologies and procedures may include value metrics, such as reduction in resource use, improvement in physician decision making, long-term and real-world effectiveness, and other patient-based outcomes.[18,19]

In fact, technologies that lack published health economic data, or for which several alternative treatments exist, are significantly less likely to be covered by CMS.[16] The need for both clinical and economic data also applies to state-based HTA (e.g., New York Medicaid).[20] A new report has focused on the impact of CER on U.S. payer decision making and assessed how payers view the importance of various study types, such as RCTs with a comparator, health economics, outcomes research, quality-of-life studies, short- and long-term head-to-head studies, meta-analyses, and retrospective observational studies, among others.[21] Key findings from this report are that in the near future formulary decision makers will be using data from many more sources to make their decisions, and CER will have a major impact on U.S. payer decision making.[21]

In addition, several public payer organizations, including CMS, have recently instituted coverage with evidence development (CED) policies, whereby national or local coverage decisions are issued conditionally if additional data (e.g., long-term, real-world registry) are collected to supplement the standard claim.[22,23,24] CED policies are also expected to become a new standard practice for private payer coverage decisions.[25]

Regarding the European Union (EU), a Conformité Européenne (CE) mark, indicating that the product has met European health or safety requirements, does not mean market access will be fully achieved. Rather, payers still want more comprehensive information to establish effectiveness and sometimes cost-effectiveness, with variation in coverage policies across individual EU member states.[8,26] In France for instance, devices must be supported by both clinical and economic data to be classified as reimbursable and included in a positive list.[26] Across Europe, if manufacturers receive coverage for a product, they are then faced with a variety of country-specific post-coverage rules and regulations.[26]

HTA agencies help to inform coverage and reimbursement decisions made by public and private payers for technologies such as medical devices. The assessments performed by these agencies incorporate expanded criteria, such as cost-effectiveness and the broader impact of medical treatments.[27] In the United Kingdom, the recently introduced National Institute for Health and Clinical Excellence (NICE) Medical Technology Evaluation Program is designed to help the National Health Services understand the budget impact and cost-effectiveness of medical devices and diagnostics for coverage and reimbursement recommendations.[28] In Canada, similar programs exist for medical devices and other non-drug technologies, such as the Ontario Health Technology Advisory Program which makes recommendations to the Ministry of Health.[29] The United States has seen the development of several HTA initiatives at federal, regional, and private levels incorporating both drug and non-drug technology assessments; this practice is expanding and is becoming more comparable in certain respects to established HTA bodies in other countries.[30,31] Overall, such groups are expected to grow in importance and expand to accommodate more timely and comprehensive evaluation relevant to medical devices for informing payer decisions.

Finally, payers are also becoming more interconnected with hospitals to control escalating health care costs. For instance, as part of U.S. health care reform, CMS is establishing value-based payment models to cut costs and improve quality of care.[32,33] Large private U.S. insurers are also aligning themselves with value-based payment models.[34]

Given these factors, it is critical that medical device manufacturers place greater emphasis on public and private payer customers. Without payer support, product awareness among physicians will be insufficient to secure market success for a new medical device.

## 3.3.2 NEW PROCESSES AND REQUIREMENTS FOR HOSPITALS

> ### Summary of New Processes and Requirements for Hospitals
>
> - Hospitals are facing increasing pressures to contain costs and optimize outcomes, causing hospital finance and materials management personnel to take on a larger role in rationing use of technologies, such as medical devices.
> - The activities of hospital decision makers center around examining whether a product's effectiveness justifies its cost. Such activities may include limiting the number of suppliers, prioritizing cost-saving devices, and rethinking purchase of physician preference items (PPIs).
> - Hospital technology assessment committees (TACs) are increasingly being used to control costs and standardize product adoption decisions. Such committees vary across countries, institutions, and device categories in their composition, processes, and evaluation criteria.

As noted earlier, for a device to be used in a procedure the physician must want to use it, the payer must provide coverage and reimbursement, and the hospital must make the device available by purchasing it. However, hospitals, like the rest of the health care sector, are facing increasing pressures to contain costs and optimize patient outcomes. These pressures are translating into hospitals shifting their decision-making strategies to control costs.[10,35,36] In response, hospital finance and materials management personnel are taking on a larger role in rationing investments in clinical technologies, including medical devices. In fact, these budget pressures are reportedly forcing many hospitals to choose between personnel and medical device purchases (quoted as "staff vs. stuff").[37]

The budget control activities of hospital decision makers may include limiting the number of suppliers for certain device categories, optimizing product use, prioritizing cost-saving technologies, freezing capital expenditures, imposing payment caps,[o] and rethinking purchase of PPIs.[p,37,38] A common theme in many of these activities involves

---

o **Payment cap:** A price ceiling for particular item categories.
p **Physician Preference Items:** Items for which physicians have strong preferences, such as spine implants, leads, bone products, heart valves, pacemakers, and stents.

examining whether the product's effectiveness justifies its cost. Essentially, for product evaluation, several value metrics, such as HTA, CEA, and BIA (including resource efficiencies and cost-offsets), are becoming more relevant. A 2009 survey of U.S. hospitals revealed that close to one-third of hospitals are adopting new data standards within the next five years.[37]

Several U.S. hospitals have recently tried to systematically gain control over purchase of everyday use or "commodity" items through strategies such as group-purchasing organizations where favorable pricing may be linked to a hospital's commitment to buy a specific volume of product.[38] While achieving contract compliance may be feasible for commodities such as bandages and syringes, hospitals are less able to ensure contract compliance for PPIs because preferences for items in the same PPI category still vary widely. A recent survey of four U.S. hospital systems reported how hospitals shape physician-induced purchasing behavior for the purpose of lowering the high cost of PPIs.[38] In brief, hospitals had begun using either formulary models[q] or payment cap models[r] as the standardization strategy.[38] Of note, the formulary model places a greater burden on physicians to adjust to a restricted set of products, as well as hospitals to more rigorously assess products' equivalency to ensure a restricted product set does not compromise patient outcomes.[38] In terms of implementing the standardization strategy, several of the facilities had some form of hospital TACs,[38] which are further described below.

## Hospital Technology Assessment Committees:

In relation to controlling hospital costs, hospital TACs (or value analysis committees [VACs]) are increasingly being used to consolidate and standardize purchasing and product adoption decisions.[1,35,38]

---

q  **Formulary Model:** Restricts the number of choices of manufacturers from which PPIs are purchased or the range of products bought for a given procedure. The assumptions underlying this approach are that a hospital's commitment to use a manufacturer will result in lower prices, that chosen vendors will have sufficient range of products to meet patients' needs, that the wide range of products on the market is unnecessary because of genuine product equivalences, and patient safety is enhanced with use of familiar products.

r  **Payment cap model:** Does not explicitly restrict particular products or manufacturers but instead standardizes costs by restricting the price paid for products in a category. The key assumption is that manufacturers of similar products will compete to offer an equivalent product within a price ceiling established for the products' specification.

The terms TACs and VACs are often used interchangeably; for consistency, TAC is used from here on.

Hospital TACs bring a systematic approach to planning and managing innovative and competitive health care technologies, such as medical devices. TACs serve as gatekeepers for the introduction of new devices to hospitals, which is analogous to the well-established model of pharmacy and therapeutics committees.[40] Processes and evaluation criteria vary according to whether a TAC is evaluating capital (e.g., robots), implants (e.g., discs, stents, pacemakers), or less expensive surgical supplies.

Committees also vary by institution. An example of how a TAC may be specifically referred to is as a "substantially equivalent committee," whereby materials management and supply chain personnel are one group involved in assessing the cost and clinical benefit of categories of "me too" 510k devices (e.g., pacemakers).[39] Further, there may be "cost center standards committees" where surgeons and materials management specialists focus on supply cost management, such as for surgery, involving devices across a number of specialties.[39]

The following steps provide an example of a workflow of a general TAC process:[39]

1. Information gathering.
2. Review period.
3. Clinical discussion (i.e., technology need, benefits, standard of care, limitations).
4. Cost data sharing.
5. Physician-aided contract negotiations with materials management/finance personnel.
6. Tracking of device use.

HTA is an evolving process in the United States, where close to 60% of hospitals now have some form of TAC.[37] More sophisticated hospital TACs may involve the assembly of a cross-functional team of expert clinicians, administrative personnel, and experts in the HTA process who will facilitate evidence-based review. Physician involvement varies depending on type of product but administrative personnel are often permanent members. Also, some U.S. hospital TACs issue only purchasing advisories for capital expenses but make actual purchasing decisions for medical devices.[40] Of noteworthy mention, TAC processes and decisions may never be visible to sales representatives.

As one example, the University of California-San Francisco multidisciplinary TAC, developed in 2006 involves physicians as well as key administrative personnel, including the chief medical and financial officers, as well as the director of materials management who also provide essential input.[41] The committee members understand that new technology may increase hospital costs. Their task is to decide whether the technology's promise of improved outcomes justifies this additional cost.[41]

As a second example, through their identification of best practices for hospital HTA, the Integrated Healthcare Association and Berkeley Center for Health Technology concluded that ideally, a TAC should both authorize an implantable device before the hospital purchase it from the device company, as well as play a role in promoting a new physician culture of cost-consciousness and comparative effectiveness.[40] In addition, they concluded that physicians interested in a new device or procedure should present it to the committee with data on its quality and price compared to other procedures or devices.[40]

Outside of the United States, hospital TACs have similar goals, with specific processes shaped by regional health care systems. Several European hospital TACs fit the model of having the long-term goal of improving quality of care with fair distribution and allocation of resources at the hospital level. A European-based study highlighted the need for hospital HTA based on two key factors: fixed budgets and competing technologies.[36] The authors significantly noted the need for hospital internal assessment processes, as reports from national or regional HTA agencies are insufficient for hospital decision-making purposes, given timing issues, as well as mismatched assessment priorities and content needs.[36] In Canada, certain provinces, such as Alberta, are incorporating more formal multidisciplinary hospital TACs, composed of clinicians, managers, and purchasing and financial experts within their regional hospitals, whereby all new technologies must be more formally evaluated before purchase.[42]

In addition to the increased use of formalized committees and evidence-based decision making as part of product adoption, hospitals will continue to use other factors in their negotiations. This may include considering the hospital's financial position (e.g., average margin on procedures involving the device) and vendor factors (e.g., quality of service, volume purchased).[39]

**The Impact of U.S. Health Reform on Hospitals**

In the United States, evidence-based product differentiation will also be critical to supporting the implementation of U.S. health reform initiatives. *Figure 3.6* provides a list of sample initiatives that are predicted to impact hospital budgets as well as increase the demand (e.g., by hospital TACs) for evidence. For instance, with value-based purchasing, payer reimbursement to hospitals will become contingent on such measures as mortality rate, hospital-associated complications (e.g., infections), patient safety indicators, and cost efficiencies.[43,44] If hospitals do not comply with such measures, reimbursement will be lower than expected. As such, product differentiation according to these factors will be critical so that hospital decision-makers understand which products can enhance quality improvement efforts.

### 3.3.3 NEW PROCESSES AND REQUIREMENTS FOR PHYSICIANS

Physicians who were pivotal in the selection of preferred devices have become less influential on product adoption within hospitals. Decision-making power is shifting towards a collaborative effort amongst physicians and hospital purchasers. This change is evident across North America and Europe.[9,35,37]

The decline of physician influence in hospitals' selection of preferred devices is due in part to changing trends in physician employment. In the past, physicians could influence hospital medical device purchasing decisions through selective referral of patients from their practices. However, the number of U.S. physicians in private practice is declining: it is expected that only 24% of physicians will own private practices in 2013.[35] As hospital employees, physicians are unable

**FIGURE 3.6** | U.S. health care reform initiatives targeted to cutting costs and improving quality and efficiency will challenge hospital budgets and drive demand for evidence-based product value differentiation[33,44]

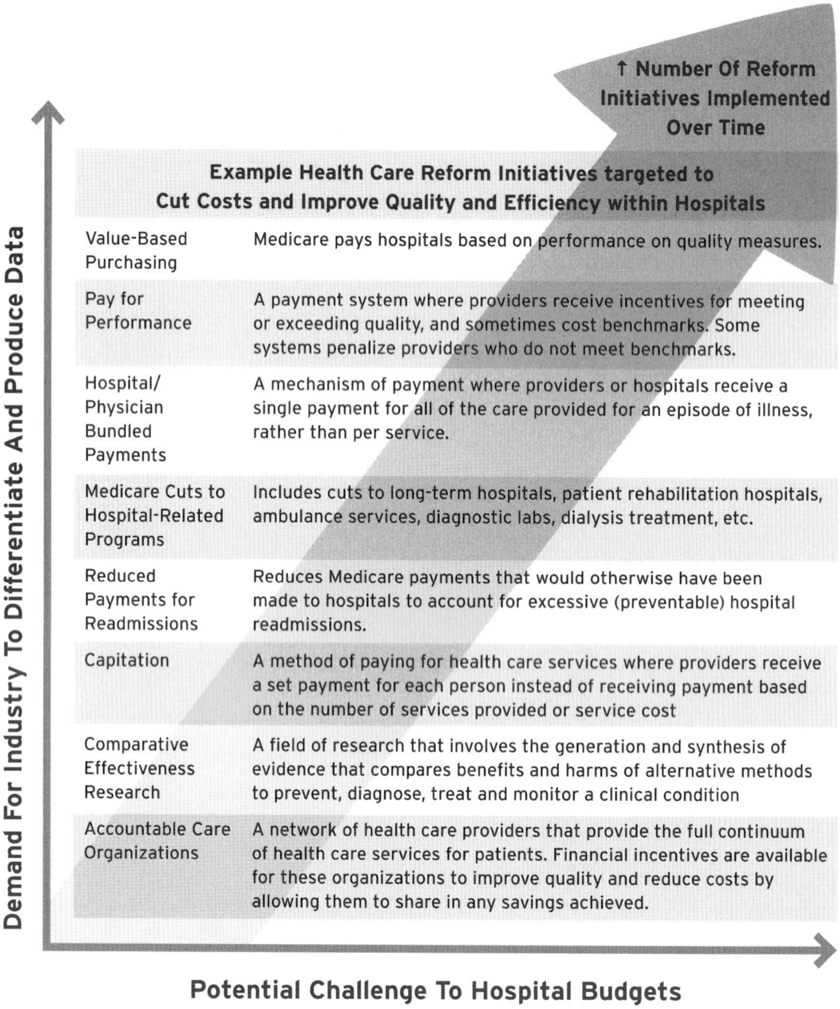

Number Of Reform Initiatives Implemented Over Time

**Demand For Industry To Differentiate And Produce Data** (vertical axis)

**Example Health Care Reform Initiatives targeted to Cut Costs and Improve Quality and Efficiency within Hospitals**

| | |
|---|---|
| Value-Based Purchasing | Medicare pays hospitals based on performance on quality measures. |
| Pay for Performance | A payment system where providers receive incentives for meeting or exceeding quality, and sometimes cost benchmarks. Some systems penalize providers who do not meet benchmarks. |
| Hospital/ Physician Bundled Payments | A mechanism of payment where providers or hospitals receive a single payment for all of the care provided for an episode of illness, rather than per service. |
| Medicare Cuts to Hospital-Related Programs | Includes cuts to long-term hospitals, patient rehabilitation hospitals, ambulance services, diagnostic labs, dialysis treatment, etc. |
| Reduced Payments for Readmissions | Reduces Medicare payments that would otherwise have been made to hospitals to account for excessive (preventable) hospital readmissions. |
| Capitation | A method of paying for health care services where providers receive a set payment for each person instead of receiving payment based on the number of services provided or service cost |
| Comparative Effectiveness Research | A field of research that involves the generation and synthesis of evidence that compares benefits and harms of alternative methods to prevent, diagnose, treat and monitor a clinical condition |
| Accountable Care Organizations | A network of health care providers that provide the full continuum of health care services for patients. Financial incentives are available for these organizations to improve quality and reduce costs by allowing them to share in any savings achieved. |

**Potential Challenge To Hospital Budgets** (horizontal axis) to easily move between hospitals; also, they are more vested in their hospital's financial decision making and may share in bonuses based on budgetary management.[14]

Although reduced, physician influence is still very important to the market success of medical devices. Physicians remain the experts in evaluating the potential clinical value of an innovative medical device and its actual value in everyday use, and will play a critical, evaluation-based role within emerging hospital TACs. Further, physicians are increasingly being tasked with improving hospital efficiencies. For example, in 2010, the Cleveland Clinic in the United States tasked its vascular surgeon staff with extracting $100 million in costs from the health system's supply chain by 2012.[13] In addition, some hospitals are increasingly sharing medical device prices with physicians in fostering collaborative efforts on cost containment.[1]

### 3.3.4 NEW POWER OF PATIENTS AS CUSTOMERS

Patients are becoming increasingly knowledgeable consumers. A 2008 survey of medical device manufacturers reported that patients, and patient organization or advocacy groups, were considered as separate customers within the industry.[9] The issue of device pricing and consumers is emerging as patients become aware of the costs of devices used in their care.

In regions such as the United States, more treatment costs are shifting to patients through new health insurance products such as Health Savings Accounts.[12] This shift can be anticipated to affect device costs to some extent, as patients and physicians actively evaluate competitive prices and product quality.[12] Along with patients and advocacy groups, other influencers include employers who purchase insurance products. Any (indirect) patient influence on hospital administrators typically comes through the hospitals' physicians.[15]

Finally, from a U.S. perspective, health care reform has been largely focused on the patient. For instance, the Patient-Centered Outcomes Research Institute, which was set up as part of health care reform, is an independent organization that commissions research that is guided by patients, caregivers, and the broader health care community.[45]

### 3.3.5 NEW DATA NEEDS FOR ESTABLISHING PRODUCT VALUE

Given the current requirements of payers, hospitals, physicians and patients, medical device marketing needs are shifting from attaining physician/surgeon interest to understanding, collating, and communicating data supporting a product's entire clinical and economic value. Developing the value proposition involves utilizing new value metrics across the spectrum, such as HTA, CER, CEA, patient outcomes, and budget impact. Stakeholders and customers want clinically superior products that fulfill relevant patient needs versus alternative therapies, often requesting real-world comparative data (e.g., CER). Further, translating clinical benefits and product differentiation into an economic argument, such as reduction in hospital resource use, is becoming essential to succeeding in the marketplace. The HTA of procedures involving medical devices, used to inform payer reimbursement decisions in several developed country regions, is requiring both clinical and economic (e.g., cost-effectiveness) data. As a result, data requirements are rising considerably for manufacturers of medical devices.

## REFERENCES

[1] Lerner JC, et al. The consequence of secret prices: The politics of physician preference items. *Health Affairs* 2008; 27(6): 1560-5.

[2] European Parliament and the Council of the European Union. Council Directive 2007/47/EC of 5 September 2007 amending Council Directive 93/42/EEC concerning medical devices. 2007; L 247/21 pg.21. Available at: http://eur-lex.europa.eu/LexUriServ/LexUriServ.do?uri=OJ:L:2007:247:0021:0055:en:PDF. [Accessed on: March 27, 2012]

[3] Council of the European Communities. Council Directive of 20 June 1990 on the approximation of the laws of the Member States relating to active implantable medical devices (90/385/EEC). 1990; OJ L 189 pg.17. Available at: http://eur-lex.europa.eu/LexUriServ/LexUriServ.do?uri=CONSLEG:1990L0385:20071011:en:PDF. [Accessed on: March 27, 2012]

[4] European Parliament and the Council of the European Union. Council Directive 98/79/EC of 27 October 1998 on the in vitro diagnostic medical devices. 1998; C 242/39 pg.39. Available at: http://eur-lex.europa.eu/LexUriServ/LexUriServ.do?uri=OJ:C:2011:242:0039:0043:EN:PDF. [Accessed on: March 27, 2012]

[5] Canadian Health Services Research Foundation. CHSRF series on cost drivers and health system efficiency: Hospital payment mechanisms: An overview and options for Canada. 2011; 4. Available at: http://www.chsrf.ca/Libraries/Hospital_Funding_docs/CHSRF-Sutherland-HospitalFundingENG.sflb.ashx [ Accessed on: March 27, 2012]

[6] Surgical Futures. Medicare inpatient prospective hospital payment system. 2012. Available at: http://surgicalfutures.com/2/medicare-inpatient-hospital-prospective-payment-system. [Accessed on: March 27, 2012]

[7] Baumler M. Differences among reimbursement schemes for medical devices in Europe. ISPOR 11th Annual European Congress, Athens Greece. November 8-11, 2008. Available at: http://www.together4healthinnovation.eu/uploads/ISPOR%2008/Reimbursement%20of%20MDs%20in%20Europe%20by%20M%20%20Baumler%20(TUB).pdf. [Accessed on: March 27, 2012]

8   Hagle U & Woods K. Europe's medical device industry: Leadership challenges in a changing world. *Korn/Ferry Institute*. February 2011. Available at: http://www.kornferryinstitute.com/files/pdf1/Europes_medical_device_industry_leadership_challenges_in_a_changing_world.pdf. [Accessed on: March 27, 2012]

9   Awopetu B, in collaboration with MDD EXEC and AZ Associates. Selling devices and diagnostics: The world is changing. Results from a recent survey of medical executives. 2008. Available at: http://www.pm360online.com/files/medDevice.pdf. [Accessed on: March 27, 2012]

10  Management Centre Europe. Re-inventing medical devices. 5 major simultaneous changes in the medical device industry: How will you and your company deal with them? 2011; 37.

11  Acuin JM, et al. Money and staff physicians' request determine decisions to buy medical devices. ISPOR Asia-Pacific Conference, Japan. September 2003. PHP15.

12  Reaven NL. The dilemma of medical device pricing in the USA: Using value-based pricing to support product positioning. *J Med Dev Reg*. November 2006; 3(4):26-34. Available at: http://www.strathealth.com/images/pdf/Reaven_JMDRNov06.pdf. [Accessed on: March 27, 2012]

13  U.S. Government Accountability Office. Report to the Chairman, Committee on Finance, U.S. Senate: Medicare: Lack of price transparency may hamper hospitals' ability to be prudent purchasers of implantable medical devices. January 2012; GAO-12-126. Available at: http://www.gao.gov/assets/590/587688.pdf. [Accessed on: March 27, 2012]

14  Weaver C. Study: Hospitals overpay for devices. *The Wall Street Journal: Health Industry*. February 3, 2012. Available at: http://online.wsj.com/article/SB10001424052970204662204577199431130637776.html. [Accessed on: March 27, 2012]

15  MarkeTech Group, Inc. Medical technology: Who is the customer? *The MarkéTech Group Minute*. Spring 2006; 6(1). Available at: http://www.themarketechgroup.com/doc/minutes/tmtg-min16.pdf. [Accessed on: March 27, 2012]

16  Chambers JD, et al. Factors predicting Medicare national coverage: An empirical analysis. *Med Care* 2012; 50:249-56.

17  The Advisory Board Company. Navigating the new Eea of technology assessment. June 17, 2010. (Citing: 2009 Hip and Knee Implant Review. *Orthopedic Network News*. July 2009; 20(3):1-3.

18  Centers for Medicare & Medicaid Services. The use of ECG based signal analysis technologies to detect myocardial ischemia or coronary artery disease. MEDCAC Meeting 11/9/2011. Available at: https://www.cms.gov/medicare-coverage-database/details/medcac-meeting-details.aspx?MEDCACId=61&TimeFrame=7&DocType=All&bc=AQAA1AAAAAAA&. [Accessed on: March 27, 2012]

19  Hogan M. MedCAC calls for more research on catheter ablation for atrial fibrillation. Medical Device Today. October 26, 2009. Available at: http://www.medicaldevicestoday.com/2009/10/medcac-calls-for-more-research-on-catheter-ablation-for-atrial-fibrillation-.html. [Accessed on: March 27, 2012]

20  New York State Department of Health, Medicaid Redesign Team. Basic Benefit Review Work Group. Final recommendations. November 1, 2011. Available at: http://www.health.ny.gov/health_care/medicaid/redesign/docs/basic_benefit_review_wrk_grp_final_rpt.pdf. [Accessed on: March 27, 2012]

21  Industry Standard Research. US payers indicate comparative effectiveness research gaining importance: Informing the drug development and commercialization industry. The Wall Street Journal: Market Watch. January 17, 2012. Available at: http://www.marketwatch.com/story/isr-us-payers-indicate-comparative-effectiveness-research-gaining-importance-2012-01-17. [Accessed on: March 27, 2012]

22  Centers for Medicare & Medicaid Services. Coverage with evidence development. Available at: https://www.cms.gov/CoverageGenInfo/03_CED.asp. [Accessed on: March 27, 2012]

23  Levin L, et al. Coverage with evidence development: The Ontario experience. *Int J Technol Assess Health Care*. 2011; 27(2):159-68.

24  Hogan M, et al. Transcatheter valve coverage proposal reflects stricter Medicare environment. *The Gray Sheet*. February 13, 2012; 38(7): # 01120213007. Available at: http://www.elsevierbi.com/publications/the-gray-sheet/38/07/transcatheter-valve-coverage-proposal-reflects-stricter-medicare-environment. [Accessed on: March 27, 2012]

25  Sparks J, et al. Reimbursement and coverage strategies matter: Here's why. Medical Device and Diagnostic Industry. December 8, 2011. Available at: http://www.mddionline.com/article/reimbursement-and-coverage-strategies-matter-heres-why. [Access March 27, 2012].

26  Schreyögg J, et al. Balancing adoption and affordability of medical devices in Europe. *Health Policy* 2009; 92(2-3):218-24.

27  Sorensen C, et al. Applying health economics for policy decision making: Do devices differ from drugs? *Europace* 2011; 13(supp 2):ii54-8.

[28] NICE. Medical Technology Evaluation Programme. November 30, 2011. Available at: http://www.nice.org.uk/aboutnice/whatwedo/aboutmedicaltechnologies/medicaltechnologiesprogramme.jsp. [Accessed on: March 27, 2012]

[29] Ontario Health Technology Advisory Committee. OHTAC recommendations. Ontario Ministry of Health and Long-Term Care. 2012. Available at: http://www.hqontario.ca/en/mas/ohtac_recommend_mn.html. [Accessed on: March 27, 2012]

[30] Eddy D. Health technology assessment and evidence-based medicine: What are we talking about? *Value Health* 2009; 12(supp 2):S6-S7.

[31] Sullivan SD, et al. Health technology assessment in health care decisions in the United States. *Value Health* 2009; 12(supp 2):S39-S44.

[32] Hart Health Strategies. PPACA: A closer look. Value-based payment modifier under the physician fee schedule. July 28, 2010. Available at: http://primaryimmune.org/advocacy_center/pdfs/health_care_reform/Value%20Based%20Purchasing%20UPDATED_20100728.pdf. [Accessed on: March 27, 2012].

[33] The Henry J. Kaiser Family Foundation. Implementation timeline. Health Reform Source. Available at: http://healthreform.kff.org/Timeline.aspx. [Accessed on: March 27, 2012]

[34] United Healthcare Services, Inc. Shifting from fee-for-service to value-based contracting model. 2012; UHCEW562088-000. Available at: http://consultant.uhc.com/assets/vbc_overview_flier.pdf. [Accessed on: March 27, 2012]

[35] Ernst & Young. Pulse of the industry: Medical technology report. EYGM Limited. 2011; (FN0008) 1107-1271824_SF. Available at: http://www.ey.com/Publication/vwLUAssets/Pulse_of_the_industry/$FILE/Pulse-of-the-industry.pdf. [Accessed on: March 27, 2012]

[36] Sampietro-Colom L. Mini-health technology assessment: A successful history in Europe. The 9th Annual Meeting of HTAi, Bilbao, Spain. June 24th, 2012. Available at: http://edma-ivd.eu/component/docman/cat_view/3-public-events?Itemid. [Accessed on: March 27, 2012]

[37] Ferenc J. Cost cuts to stay: Perfect storm of economic circumstances brings unprecedented focus on reducing spending on medical equipment and supplies. *Health Facilities Management Magazine.* December 2009; 20-26. Available at: http://www.mhsinc.com/utilities/articles/cost_cuts_to_stay.pdf. [Accessed on: March 27, 2012]

[38] Montgomery K & Schneller ES. Hospitals' strategies for orchestrating selection of physician preference items. *The Milbank Quarterly* 2007; 85(2):307-35.

[39] The Advisory Board Company. Navigating the new era of technology assessment. June 17, 2010.

[40] Integrated Healthcare Associations and the Berkeley Centre for Health Technology. Physician-hospital alignment in the evaluation, purchasing and use of implantable medical devices. October 2, 2009. Available at: http://www.berkeleyhealthtech.org/docs/Vol.2.1.Implantable_Devices.pdf. [Accessed on: March 27, 2012]

[41] Gutowsky C, et al. Health technology assessment at the University of California – San Fransico. *J Healthc Manag.* 2011; 56(1):15-29; discussion 29-30.

[42] Poulin P, et al. HTA into practice: 5 years of local HTA program in a surgical department. Alberta Health Services. Presented at CADTH Symposium, Vancouver, BC. April 3-5, 2011; A3. Available at: http://www.cadth.ca/media/symp-2011/present/A3%20HTA%20In%20Hospitals%20-%20Poulin.pdf. [Accessed on: March 27, 2012]

[43] Studer Group. Value-based purchasing at a glance: What the final rule means for your organization. Available at: http://www.studergroup.com/wrihc2011/resources/VBPAtAGlance.pdf. [Accessed on: March 27, 2012]

[44] Pham H, et al. Episode-based payments: Charting a course for health care payment reform. National Institute For Health Care Reform. *Policy Analysis.* January 2010; 1:1-16.

[45] Patient-Centered Outcomes Research Institute. About us. Available at: http://www.pcori.org/about. [Accessed on: March 27, 2012]

# CHAPTER 4

# An Integrated Solution for the Changed Medical Device Industry

## KEY MESSAGE:

An integrated solution that develops and communicates product value to payers and purchasers can provide a competitive advantage in today's medical device market. This solution involves ongoing assessment starting at the early stages of development, a comprehensive evidence development phase, the development of communication tools, and a targeted system for communicating value to customers and other relevant stakeholders.

## CONCEPTS DISCUSSED:

The solution includes three key categories, discussed in the context of examples:
- Assess customers' and other stakeholders' perspectives, unmet needs, market potential, reimbursement framework, and evidence needs.
- Build evidence base, value proposition, pricing strategy, reimbursement plan, and communication tools.
- Communicate evidence-based product value to customers and other stakeholders.

Unique activities, according to each category, are discussed for products at specific pre- and post-launch time points.

**FIGURE 4.1 |** Detailed framework for market access success in the Value Era.

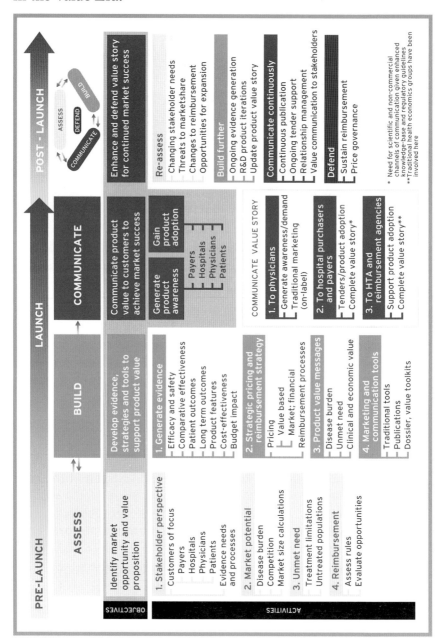

Given the recent changes in industry customers, evaluation processes, and evidence needs, market adoption of medical devices may be threatened if companies do not adapt their strategies and processes. This chapter proposes a holistic strategy designed to achieve market success in this new environment.

In the current Value Era, medical device manufacturers require new multifaceted structures that foster innovative thinking and maximize synergies with existing development and commercialization functions. Creating and executing a strategy that meets these requirements can provide a competitive advantage in the marketplace. *Figure 4.1* presents a flowchart that delineates the process anticipated to meet these new demands. This framework presupposes that activities should be conducted on the basis of a holistic market access plan; with continuous evaluation of how efficiencies can be maximized across all medical devices a company is developing and manufacturing. The framework is divided into pre- and post-launch activities and emphasizes the need to continuously assess, build, and communicate evidence that is based on product value.

## 4.1 | ASSESS Pre-Launch

**ASSESS:** The objective of this phase is to identify market opportunities, customer needs, the potential value proposition for the medical device, and evidence needs to support value. The value proposition is a set of product value messages based on the evidence.

Early and continuous assessment of a device in relation to the clinical and reimbursement environments is critical to success in the Value Era. The medical device market has become more restrictive, with an evolving customer base and expanded evidence requirements. This assessment phase thus needs to occur before substantial investment in product development. In relation to this, recent global surveys in the biopharmaceutical industry have identified that companies are waiting too long to involve market access functions, such as health economics and reimbursement.[1,2] As well, it has been suggested that meetings with payers to discuss unmet needs and evidence requirements to support reimbursement often occur too close to launch, which leaves insufficient opportunity to conduct evidence generation.[1,2]

Early assessment regarding the device, through a range of health economics and other activities (see *Figure 4.2*), can allow the company to answer the following overall key questions:

- Will the expected marketing messages for the device be acceptable to payers and supported by evidence during health technology assessments (HTAs)?

- Will potential restrictions on market access limit the pricing or sales of the device?

- Given potential market access or pricing limitations, is the device a good candidate for further development?

- What is required to maximize the perceived value of the product to payers and purchasers?

- Given the device development pipeline, and the comparative market potential of such products, how should resources best be allocated?

**FIGURE 4.2 | The ASSESS phase (pre-launch): Description of objectives and activities.**

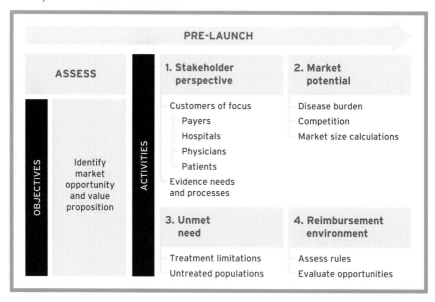

During the assessment phase, activities can be grouped into categories, each with its own set of critical questions: stakeholder perspectives, market potential and unmet need, and reimbursement environment.

## 4.1.1 ASSESSING STAKEHOLDER PERSPECTIVES

Key questions related to assessing stakeholder perspectives are:

- What is the customer mix for this device type?
- Which customers have the greatest influence on adoption of this device?
- What decision-making processes exist for hospital accounts?
- Given the device type, what data are most relevant for these customers? How do these data differ from regulatory requirements?
- What is the optimal process for communicating data to each customer type?
- What other factors involved in decision making for this device, beyond product value, are important for adoption (e.g., hospital financial objectives)?

A fundamental role for a medical device market access program is to understand the customer mix, which includes payers, hospitals, patients, and physicians, and also how the influence of each customer varies by type of medical device. For instance, for highly innovative products, physician demand may be an important factor in decision making. This may apply to the first medical device of its kind or a medical device for a small, well-differentiated patient population with a limited number of treating physicians. For devices with multiple competitors or a large market size (e.g., coronary stents), hospital procurement may play a central role in evaluating the relative value of products and deciding on adoption. It is also important to realize that the relative importance of the physician and hospital purchaser will vary by region and account; as such, strategies will need to be adapted across hospitals.

When considering a hospital customer, a company must be aware of the variation that exists between accounts in terms of evidence assessment. In some instances, a sophisticated hospital committee that makes purchasing decisions (e.g., technology assessment or value-analysis committee) may be present, often composed of physician and/or administrative members, while others will have no such formalized body and only one or two key decision makers (e.g., head of surgery, procurement manager). Understanding who the customers are and how they interact in the decision-making process will help dictate the types of internal resources that will be most effective.

In addition to identifying the key customer and the decision processes, a company must consider what data are required and how these data may differ from what is being collected for regulatory audiences. For instance, if the product is associated with a large acquisition cost, hospital decision makers may want to know how using this product will result in hospital-related resource efficiencies to generate a return on investment. Public payers, such as the Centers for Medicare & Medicaid Services (CMS), may prefer evidence of the comparative effectiveness of the product relative to all current treatment options, which is typically beyond the evidence that is collected for regulatory approval. Private payers often follow public payer processes; thus, similar strategies and information may be required. Knowing the evidence requirements early in product development will help to inform clinical trial or registry design, so that relevant evidence is available in a timely manner and data quality may be maximized.

Finally, understanding the processes for communicating the product value proposition (i.e., a set of value messages based on evidence) to customers will allow optimization of the value communication plan. As discussed, hospital committee requirements and processes are expanding and will likely vary by region and hospital setting. Examples of some important questions to answer for key hospital accounts may include: How do processes for review vary by medical device category? What triggers hospital committee review of a product? How do committees obtain information needed to perform analyses? How can a company best provide data to the customer?

## 4.1.2 ASSESSING MARKET POTENTIAL AND UNMET NEED

Key questions related to market potential and unmet need are:

- What is the disease burden associated with untreated or unsuccessfully treated patients?
- What comprises current care and the standard of care for the condition being treated by the device under development?
- What is the strength of the evidence for the competition?
- What are the existing unmet needs that the new medical device could address?
- What data are required to demonstrate fulfillment of these unmet needs?
- What is the potential market size and pricing for this product?

In planning for the development of an evidence base that will support a device's place in therapy, it is necessary to precisely define the existing disease burden, which includes morbidity, mortality, and health-related quality of life (HRQOL) impacts. The disease burden may apply to the entire patient population, or may be specific to a subpopulation with an unmet need (e.g., unsuccessfully treated patients or patents ineligible for standard care). This process of defining the disease burden can identify outcomes that need to be evaluated in the clinical program. The disease burden directly informs the potential value proposition and pricing for a new device.

Understanding the current competition and predicting how it may change are fundamental to informing whether comparative studies are required and how these studies need to be designed. For instance, if there is one main competitor for the new device, direct comparison of efficacy and safety through a randomized controlled trial (RCT) may be possible and could be important in securing reimbursement by payers and adoption by hospitals. If a new device has multiple competitors, conducting head-to-head RCTs against all competitors will not be feasible, and alternative methods of comparison, such as indirect treatment comparisons (ITCs) or mixed treatment comparisons (MTCs), may be required. It is also important to understand the strength of the evidence supporting the competition. Clearly, a strong evidence base for a competitor increases the data needs for a new device and increases the costs and challenges of entry into the area.

With knowledge of the current treatment environment, the potential unmet clinical need in the area can be assessed. An unmet need can be interpreted in several ways, such as absence of treatment for the condition, high risk of complications with current devices, opportunity for improvement in efficacy, and difficulty in operator device use. In understanding the unmet clinical needs, companies can design studies to provide evidence that demonstrates that the new device addresses these needs.

Finally, market size needs to be assessed. Market size can often be difficult to assess if the device is first to market or is addressing a narrow patient subpopulation. In both cases, epidemiological, database, market research and/or chart review activities may be required to develop a defensible estimate of market size. In addition to this, the reimbursement environment, discussed in the next section, can alter the "effective" market size.[3] Together, these are critical factors for consideration in decisions about whether to proceed with a new technology.

### 4.1.3 ASSESSING THE REIMBURSEMENT ENVIRONMENT

The goal of evaluating the reimbursement environment is to ensure that reimbursement of the new medical device can be optimized and thereby more readily adopted by hospitals.

Key questions related to assessing the reimbursement environment are:

- How are competitor products currently covered and reimbursed?

- Are existing procedure codes (e.g., ICD-9 or ICD-10)[s] applicable, or are new code(s) needed?

- If new procedure codes are needed, what type of evidence is required to support this need?

- Are reimbursement rules set up in a manner that will accommodate the new device?

---

[s] **ICD 9 CM:** A standardized classification of diseases, injuries, and causes of death, by etiology and anatomic localization and codified into a 6-digit number, which allows clinicians, statisticians, politicians, health planners, and others to speak a common language (primarily in the United States). The International Classification of Diseases (ICD) has been revised periodically to incorporate changes in the medical field. The Tenth Revision (ICD-10) differs from the Ninth Revision (ICD-9) in several ways, mainly to allow increased specificity, although the overall content is similar.

- Could early data supporting the additional costs of a transformational new procedure/device be helpful in achieving more rapid reimbursement that will adequately cover the new costs?

- Is the expected reimbursement payment for the procedure/device acceptable to hospital decision makers?

- Is the payment classification (e.g., DRG[t]) for which the product is mapped sufficient to cover the costs of the device by the hospital? If insufficient, how can the amount be increased?

- Will the hospital realize any cost savings beyond the procedure (e.g., recovery time, length of stay) related to medical device use, which may impact adoption decisions?

The success of devices used in hospitals often depends on adequate payer reimbursement. According to whether payer reimbursement is specific to the device versus the procedure involving the device, a comprehensive set of rules will need to be understood. If the new device will compete with existing devices, then their reimbursement will provide insights into challenges and opportunities for the reimbursement of the new device. In many cases, the new device will address an unmet need for a procedure that already exists and is reimbursed. The device reimbursement strategy may be built based upon the assumption that the procedure reimbursement will provide sufficient funding to a hospital to purchase the new device. Alternatively, the strategy may require creation of new procedure codes and/or reimbursement payment codes for the use of the new device.

A critical first step involves understanding the adequacy of procedural coding from the hospital perspective, in addition to that of the treating physician (e.g., CPT-4[u]). Procedure codes specify the affected body part and describe the treatment or surgery.[4] If the existing

---

[t] **Diagnosis-related group (DRG):** A system to classify hospital cases into one of several groups. DRGs are assigned by a "grouper" program based on ICD diagnoses, procedures, age, sex, discharge status, and the presence of complications or co-morbidities. DRGs have been used in the United States since 1982 to determine how much Medicare pays the hospital for each service, since patients within each category are clinically similar and are expected to use the same level of hospital resources.

[u] **CPT-4:** Current Procedural Terminology is a system developed by the American Medical Association for standardizing the terminology and coding used to describe medical services and procedures;. CPT can be used for hospital outpatient and physician fee schedules.

coding structure does not adequately describe the procedure and how the new medical device will be used, companies should request a new or revised procedure code.

A current example of this situation is transcatheter aortic valve replacement. Procedure codes for surgical valve replacement have been in existence for decades, but devices have only recently been approved for the transcatheter procedural approach, which has necessitated the creation of new procedure codes.[5,6] Understanding the evidence requirements for obtaining new procedure codes is clearly a necessary step for such transformational devices.

Another example involved the advent of coronary drug-eluting stents (DES). While an existing procedure code adequately described the implantation of a coronary bare-metal stent (BMS), it did not satisfactorily describe the clinically proven transformational aspects of this initial drug-device combination product. If the procedure code for a coronary BMS were utilized, recognizing the incremental value of the DES would have posed significant challenges, since tracking the use of this new device would have been extremely difficult. Therefore, a separate procedure code was established to differentiate between the implantation of a DES and BMS.[7]

Payers frequently use procedure codes to determine whether a particular technology is a covered benefit, as well as to specify the rate of payment to hospitals and physicians.[4] From a strategic standpoint, medical device companies must evaluate whether payer coverage and/ or payment rate challenges exist before making a final decision on the appropriateness of an existing procedure code.

Regarding the stenting example previously described, DES and BMS had not only unique procedure codes but unique payments as well in the United States. In countries where different DES are reimbursed with an identical payment amount, reimbursement processes were simplified with subsequent DES that came on the market. However, there was, and continues to be, variation in the hospital acquisition cost of different DES. This is commonly observed with a number of device categories, where similar devices may be available at different prices. In these cases, it is critical for device manufacturers to clearly differentiate their product based on product attributes, clinical and economic evidence, and a strong product value proposition. Otherwise the hospital decision makers may perceive profit loss if they contemplate adopting a more expensive device that would not be fully reimbursed.

Finally, often a lag time exists before hospitals are adequately reimbursed for a new procedure/device, as occurred with the advent of DES. This lag time can occur because data need to be gathered to inform the payment mechanism and amounts. In some cases, acquiring knowledge of the actual hospital-related costs involved with the entire procedure, as part of clinical studies, may help to provide real-cost data to payers to expedite the payment processes.

### 4.1.4 TIMING OF ACTIVITIES

The ASSESS phase should be part of internal processes that involve setting investment priorities for pre-clinical and clinical research or considering a product for in-licensing. At this stage, product market potential may be evaluated based on market size, target population market share, and expected price. Both marketshare and expected price are dependent on the product's evidence and value proposition; in many markets, they are also dependent on the product's potential for reimbursement and market access. As discussed in *Chapter 2*, a product with low perceived value relative to its price will face market restrictions by payers, which will undermine the product's sales potential. The consideration of price potential in relation to payer demands may compliment internal efforts to optimize product development budgets. Overlooking this criterion is one of the most common failures of the industry, leading to acquisition prices for in-licensed products, as well as ill-informed research and development (R&D) decisions, which do not reflect true market potential.

The ASSESS phase extends to the time of product launch. Continual re-assessment will allow the optimization of the device value proposition and evidence base. It also ensures that changes in the marketplace due to legislation, competitors, and policies are captured and appropriate adjustments are made.

ASSESS activities may include systematic literature reviews, payer advisory boards and surveying, development of projected product value messages to identify data gaps and align messaging, design of exploratory value-based pricing models, sales forecasts, analysis of the value of information, extensive uncertainty testing for all quantitative assessments, and development of a strategic plan that includes evidence generation, pricing, reimbursement, and communication.

## 4.2 | BUILD Pre-Launch to Launch

**BUILD:** The objective of this phase is to primarily develop evidence and communication tools for the medical device that will support the device's value proposition, and the related strategic pricing and reimbursement processes.

**FIGURE 4.3 | The BUILD phase (pre-launch to launch):** Description of objectives and activities.

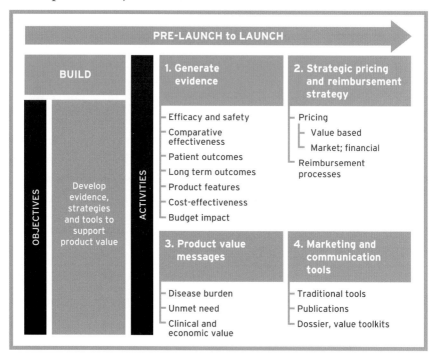

As evidence beyond traditional clinical trial data is required in many markets for reimbursement, it is critical to initiate several evidence-generating activities early in the pre-launch phase. The BUILD phase should develop the evidence base, considering relevant customer requirements and the type of medical device, and bundle the evidence into appropriate tools for communication (see *Figure 4.3*). The majority of these activities are informed by completing the tasks outlined in the ASSESS phase.

## 4.2.1 EVIDENCE GENERATION

Evidence generation needs to involve data collection and analysis that will support the clinical and economic value of the medical device compared to relevant alternative treatments, and according to outcomes that are pertinent to today's customers. A wide array of study designs can be used to support such evidence generation (see *Figure 4.4*). The selection of the studies depends in part on the medical device type and on the unmet clinical need. Aligning studies with traditional health technology assessment and health economic requirements, as well as emerging comparative effectiveness expectations, can ensure development of a full-value proposition.

It is important to consider the challenges with developing an evidence base for a device using RCTs. These studies are unlikely to provide data against the full scope of competitors, especially given the rapid development time of devices. For instance, devices frequently undergo product modifications that may affect device performance and safety.[8,9] As such, it may be challenging to conduct RCTs on all device iterations. In addition, the competitors for a device will rapidly change, making it difficult – if not impossible – to compare all relevant alternatives within one RCT. As well, efficacy often depends not only on the device itself but also on how it is used (i.e., operator learning curves) which may create bias.[9] Collectively, these factors are expected to impact the quality and quantity of RCT data available. To address such challenges in data development for medical devices, it is important to utilize other methodological approaches, such as real-world observational studies and other types of comparative effectiveness study designs (e.g., meta-analyses, ITCs).[8] Following is an explanation of each type of category outlined in *Figure 4.4.*

### Efficacy and Safety

In the United States, the Pre-Market Application requirement for devices is that a new or modified device is safe and efficacious, as demonstrated through pre-clinical and clinical data.[10] Of lesser stringency, the 510(k) clearance requires evidence that the device is substantially

**FIGURE 4.4 |** Evidence generation for medical devices – demonstrating value.

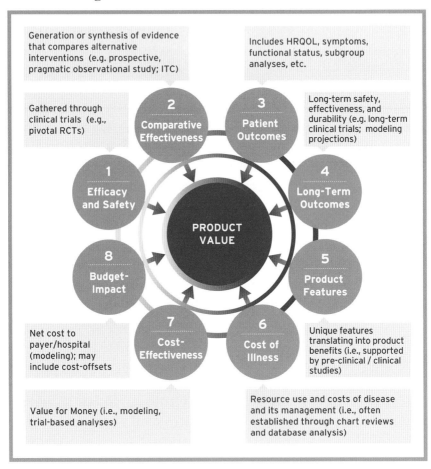

equivalent compared to a predicate device, typically only requiring laboratory data. In either case, manufacturers generate such data to be able to market the device in the United States. In Europe, data requirements for receiving a Conformité Européenne (CE) mark may be less stringent.[10]

Observational data, such as prospective registries or chart reviews, are often used to supplement the efficacy and safety data by adding longer-term follow-up in broader patient populations. For example, a study of a new therapy for the rare condition myeloma kidney (renal failure secondary to multiple myeloma-related free light chain overproduction) added extensively to the data for efficacy and safety through the use of a multi-country chart review.[11] This study supplemented the limited data available at launch.[12]

## Comparative Effectiveness Research (CER)

As defined in *Chapter 2*, CER involves the comparison of relevant treatment alternatives. Although such research is not a requirement of regulatory approval, it is fast becoming an expectation – and in some cases a requirement – of payers, hospitals and physicians. In an environment of budget restrictions and high competition, this type of research is a must-have for product success. Systematic reviews, analyses of hospital records, prospective pragmatic trials or observational studies, and ITCs are some study designs that can be used to address the comparative effectiveness of devices. These studies fill gaps in the evidence base after completion of the RCTs. The gaps do not represent a failing of the RCTs; instead, they represent the practical limitations of RCTs for medical devices as discussed in previous sections.

DES are an example of a device category whereby several comparators exist and, as such, adjusted ITCs[13,14] and network meta-analyses[15] have been used to more clearly establish comparative effectiveness in broad and specific patient populations. Recent research has dedicated efforts toward developing high-quality CER designs involving ITCs.[16]

## Patient Outcomes

Patient outcomes typically involve a unique set of endpoints that are relevant to patients and may often be reported by the patients themselves (i.e., patient-reported outcomes (PROs)). In general, patient outcomes include an individual's preferences, autonomy, and needs and focus on outcomes that patients care about, such as survival, function and disability, symptoms, and HRQOL. Studies centered on patient outcomes may incorporate a wide variety of settings and population types to address individual differences. In an era where the importance of patients as customers is growing, and national organizations have been established with the mission of improving patient-centered research (e.g., Patient-Centered Outcomes Research Institute (PCORI)), such outcomes are critical to development of the full product value proposition.

Patient outcomes data, such as PRO endpoints, can be collected within the clinical trial, as part of an extension study or within observational studies or surveys. Such data can help to determine whether improvements in trial-based clinical endpoints translate into an impact on outcomes that matter to the patient. For example, a recent study found that phakic intraocular lenses not only improved uncorrected distance visual acuity, but also was associated with patient–reported improvement in vision-related quality of life.[17] In a competitive market, such data may allow differentiation from alternative devices of corrective procedures.

## Long-Term Clinical Outcomes

Generally absent at the time of market approval, long-term data on product effectiveness and safety in the real world is an integral factor in optimizing and maintaining product value after launch. Such data can help to establish the rarity or absence of delayed adverse events (e.g., stent thrombosis), the maintenance of device effectiveness (e.g., reducing stroke risk, continued symptom relief), the improvement in operator ease of use with experience, and the durability of the product (e.g., the device remains intact if implanted internally).

Long-term outcomes data can be collected through prospective trial-based or observational studies. Alternatively, modeling can be used to predict the long-term impact of a device in the absence of data. For example, the myeloma kidney product, noted earlier, resulted in a substantial increase in the proportion of patients recovering independent renal function after requiring dialysis, from 17% recovery with conventional care to 63% recovery with the new device. A disease simulation model was used to extrapolate these results to provide estimates of the impact on patient survival. The study found that the increase in renal recovery could be expected to translate into an increase in mean life expectancy of 32 months.[18]

Policy decisions in a number of areas of heath care are strongly influenced by disease simulation modeling, including screening and vaccination. In the case of screening, long-term studies to evaluate the ultimate clinical outcome are often not possible. For example, the U.S. blood-screening service in the mid-2000s adopted nucleic acid testing of volunteer blood for hepatitis B, hepatitis C, and human immuno-deficiency virus. The data supporting this decision were limited to test effectiveness, which describes the sensitivity and specificity of the test. A simulation study extended these test data to project the impact on infection cases and years.[19] Similarly, modeling of long-term outcomes is widely used in the evaluation of cervical cancer screening technologies.[20]

## Product Features

Some studies designed to highlight the benefits of medical device attributes do not measure clinical endpoints commonly used in RCTs. However, this does not mean that these benefits do not affect product selection or overall clinical outcomes. Thus, the differentiation of product features should be considered when demonstrating the value of a medical device. Such attributes can include: (1) features that promote operator ease of use (e.g., one-step deployment); (2) ergonomics; (3) enhanced technical specifications (e.g., power range, degrees of movement); (4) a wide range of options within a product family (e.g., multiple mapping and ablation catheter options for use with a mapping system); and (5) features that promote patient comfort (e.g., cushioned straps).

Studies can be conducted to provide evidence to support the benefits of product features and to bridge the gap between attributes and clinical endpoints. For example, bench-top studies may be used to assess and compare the compliance and crossing profiles, or inflation characteristics, of various balloon catheters for stenting. These data may then be used to predict or support clinical endpoints related to deployment success. Further, circular catheters used in ablation provide another example. If circular catheters are significantly associated with reduced procedure time and increased ablation efficacy, it would stand to reason that catheters shown to maintain their circular shape for longer periods of time in bench-top testing would be preferred.

The need for differentiation of product features in a value argument is applicable across device categories. This need may be particularly relevant for medical devices, such as balloon catheters, that undergo less scrutiny during the regulatory approval process and are thereby more limited with their evidence base.

## Cost of Illness

Cost of illness studies establish the health care resource use and the costs associated with the disease and its management. For example, the relevant costs for an artificial hip would include the associated costs of surgery, postoperative care, long-term care, surgical complications, and device failure. These data are useful in quantifying the extent of the disease burden to the health care system or payer, and will provide data inputs for cost-effectiveness and budget impact analyses.

Typical methods for cost of illness studies include chart reviews and database analyses. For example, a large U.S. claims-based study reported that restenosis and repeat revascularizations associated with BMS were important shortcomings, costing U.S. Medicare more than $700 million annually.[21] Such earlier studies supported the introduction of more expensive DES, which served to alleviate this clinical burden, with the increased DES acquisition cost being offset by savings in avoided re-interventions.

## Cost-Effectiveness

Demonstrating cost-effectiveness, or "value for money," requires that a medical device be priced appropriately for the benefits offered relative to other available devices. Cost-effectiveness data serve to inform the device's economic value proposition. Data used to inform such analyses (e.g., resource utilization, health utility) can be collected through clinical trials and non-trial studies, and combined through cost-effectiveness modeling.

Cost-effectiveness analyses (CEAs) may be utilized in a number of ways. They may be required by some payers as part of the reimbursement process, or they may be an optional component of a reimbursement submission, HTA initiative, or HTA process. They may also be used in value communication activities to: (1) highlight the clinical value of a product as observed in the trial, (2) illustrate the comparative effectiveness of a product versus its competitors by combining data from multiple trials, (3) predict the long-term benefits of the product by mathematically extending the clinical trial results, and (4) quantify the value for money of the product by demonstrating the clinical benefit gained relative to cost versus a competitor.

For example, the treatment for myeloma kidney noted earlier was evaluated in a cost-effectiveness model. This study found that the improved recovery of renal function resulted in fewer patient days on dialysis and was sufficient to completely offset the cost of the device.[22] The benefit of these types of analyses during discussion with payers and purchasers are obvious. For some types of devices, complete cost offsets may not be observed; however, incremental benefits may justify the increased acquisition cost, such as with implantable cardioverter defibrillators in certain populations.[23,24]

In addition to supporting reimbursement and product value throughout the life cycle, cost-effectiveness modeling can be useful in informing medical device strategic pricing prior to launch. This methodology is sometimes referred to as value-based pricing or simply price modeling. Such a pricing model can be used to define the thresholds for efficacy, safety, and costs that are required to demonstrate acceptable value to payers and purchasers. These analyses have been used to inform product development decisions, whereby products that are unlikely to provide sufficient value to customers at a price that would be feasible to the company are terminated early on to allow reallocation of resources. Similarly, value-based pricing can play an important role in evaluating products being considered for in-licensing.

### Budget Impact

In the new Value Era, the bottom line to most customers (i.e., public and private payers, hospital decision makers) is affordability, given budget constraints. This makes the budget impact analysis (BIA) a critical piece of evidence that is increasingly being requested by customers. Similar to CEAs, BIAs can serve a key role in communicating value by: (1) highlighting where cost may be avoided through the use of a device, and (2) allowing customization of budget impact to a specific payer/purchaser population.

For example, if a medical device has a higher acquisition or training cost, it would be very useful to highlight how these upfront costs can be partly or completely offset by savings in downstream hospital-related costs, such as hospital-acquired infections, length of stay, or readmissions. Similarly, if a new device is associated with substantial competition and comparable acquisition costs, demonstration of hospital-related cost offsets may be influential in recommending why hospitals should replace an existing device(s) with the new device. Recent studies of DES and vascular closure devices used in coronary procedures illustrate the value in demonstrating cost offsets related to avoidance of clinical events, such as re-interventions[13] and vascular complications,[25] with devices that have comparable acquisition costs.

Allowing BIAs to be customizable according to hospital-specific characteristics (e.g., population size, competitive products used, cost of treating adverse events), as well as informing them with high-quality data, is expected to increase the applicability and acceptance of such tools.

### 4.2.2 PRICING AND REIMBURSEMENT STRATEGIES

An early head start in defining and implementing pricing and reimbursement strategies will help to facilitate more timely and successful market access of medical devices.

## Strategic Pricing

The ultimate goal of a device pricing strategy should be to establish a price that is reflective of both customer and company needs. The customer wants a price that reflects the unmet needs of the target population, the clinical value of a product, and the budget constraints of the system. The company requires a price that reflects investment and a fair return on investment (ROI).

Benchmarking was a key strategy for technologies that were second or third to market.[26] Innovative products were priced based on market research with clinical audiences rather than on perceived value. However, with rising health care costs and ensuing budget constraints, public awareness and concern about medical device costs have risen. Recent U.S. government discussions have highlighted important concerns regarding the high prices hospitals and Medicare pay for certain devices and the wide discrepancy across hospitals in such device costs.[27]

As such, the landscape for medical devices has been fundamentally changed, requiring alteration of pricing strategies. Hospital financial decision makers have become increasingly price sensitive, looking not necessarily for the lowest-priced products, but rather for products whose price can be justified by the value they deliver in terms of safety, efficacy, cost offsets, and hospital efficiency. Pricing a product too high in reference to its value and available supporting evidence may cause substantial difficulties with its adoption. In contrast, pricing a product too low relative to its value may result in unnecessary financial loss.

The objective of strategic pricing is to quantify the factors comprising product value in ways that are relevant to external customers in order to inform the appropriate price for the medical device. This type of value-based pricing is primarily, but not exclusively, based on the assessable value to the customer.[26] The recommended steps in this process, described in *Table 4.1*, include activities that may be initiated in the ASSESS phase. This process requires close collaboration between the R&D, health economics, and commercial functions within industry.

**TABLE 4.1 | Recommended steps involved in strategic pricing of medical devices.**

- Traditional market research with clinical stakeholders.

- Benchmarking to identify products for comparison of regional pricing, evidence, cost-effectiveness, reimbursement, and technology appraisals.

- Consideration of development, licensing, and commercial costs, as well as target ROI.

- Comparison of target product profile and planned evidence to benchmarks.

- Creation of price corridor, based on benchmarks and market research.

- Testing of price corridor using value-based pricing (preliminary cost-effectiveness modeling). Such models can be used to define thresholds for efficacy, safety, and device price required to demonstrate acceptable value to decision makers.[28]

- Testing of pricing and targeting strategy within regional payer advisory boards to identify evidence needs and potential reimbursement hurdles.

The processes for developing evidence and setting prices need to be closely intertwined, so that evidence needs are identified and executed to support target prices. Having knowledge of different customers' definition of value (see *Chapter 2*) enables companies to collect evidence during the pre-launch phase and align that evidence with customer needs. For instance, technologies that are significant innovations that fulfill important unmet clinical needs can typically charge a premium price. Further, medical devices that can substitute for expensive procedures or reduce hospital resources (e.g., length of stay, procedure time, re-admissions) will be more attractive to hospital decision makers. For such products, a component of the pricing strategy could be determining the price point at which the new technology creates a break-even situation where cost offsets pay for the device.[26]

Although a product's clinical value has become integral to strategic pricing, other market-based and financial factors must also be taken into consideration. A company must have a clear understanding of the target gross and net profit for a product. Business model specifications for ROI involving consideration of the cost of development, production, marketing, and sales can provide the starting point for price estimations. These base price estimations can then be adjusted to reflect product value to payers and purchasers.[26]

It is further recommended that product pricing strategies be independent of reimbursement status. In the United States, for instance, most devices (e.g., implantable) are often not directly reimbursed; rather, they are embedded in reimbursement for the procedures that use them. If the clinical value of a new device exceeds that of its competition, a price premium is likely justified. This may mean that reimbursement codes for the procedure may not fully cover the new device's cost until new coding, if applicable, is in place.

Nevertheless, the price is a message to all customers about the technology's value; therefore, it must not be compromised. Until – and if – additional reimbursement is applicable, companies may need to be able to demonstrate how the additional product value translates into other cost offsets within the hospital or improvements in clinical practice that will be reflected in hospital quality statistics.

## Strategic Coverage and Reimbursement Processes

As previously discussed, the reimbursement environment is complex and involves an in-depth understanding of coverage, coding, and payment processes, as well as associated data requirements. In the BUILD phase, companies need to translate the knowledge acquired during the ASSESS phase into action. Some of the key activities include those that may be initiated in the ASSESS phase:

- Determine reimbursement and coding limitations and opportunities.
- Create global reimbursement strategies and collaborate with regional teams to accommodate local requirements.
- Develop and provide evidence to support enhanced reimbursement.
- Ensure consistency in evidence and messaging.

If new procedure codes are required, companies need to implement strategies to efficiently facilitate this process and ensure evidence is generated to support the new coding. As discussed in the next chapters, this will require the coordinated action of a centralized Health Economics (HE) team to guide strategy and evidence generation, and regional teams with in-depth knowledge of local payers. Regarding coverage decisions, evidence development may need to be initiated early in the process to supplement trial data with additional evidence relevant to payers. For reimbursement payment amounts, early evidence generation regarding hospital costs may optimize reimbursement.

### 4.2.3 PRODUCT VALUE MESSAGES

A product value proposition, which is a set of value messages primarily based on evidence, encompasses all aspects of product value relevant to key stakeholders, including physicians, patients, payers, purchasers, reimbursement panels, and HTA groups. It plays a central role in all phases of product support by:

- Guiding evidence development.

- Ensuring consistency of messaging across regions and between Health Economics and Commercial teams.

- Providing messaging that is tailored for market access audiences (e.g., payers, purchasers, reimbursement panels, HTA groups).

- Answering market questions regarding a product's clinical and economic values.

Using the knowledge acquired through the ASSESS phase as well as the evidence generated in the BUILD phase, a value proposition can be developed to support the medical device during its launch phase. This value proposition would ideally encompass all proven and, where applicable, product attribute-based device messages, considering the disease landscape and existing standard of care.

The value proposition needs to be initiated early in the product's development. During this phase, many of the value statements will be aspirational – that is, they will require evidence generation to provide support. In this way, the value proposition can guide evidence generation. It can also provide a reality check in terms of a product's market potential. Ideally, the following statements should be true:

- The condition being treated has important clinical or economic consequences.

- There is a clear unmet clinical need that the product will meet.

- The target population is well defined and characterized in terms of epidemiology, clinical endpoints, symptoms, HRQOL, and cost of disease.

- The trial will provide evidence of impact on recognized clinical endpoints.

- Such trial endpoints can be translated into meaningful outcomes, such as disease progression, morbidity, mortality, or procedure efficiency.

- The device will have clinical data that will facilitate CER and HTA.

- The device will have clinical and other advantages over competitive devices or procedures.

- The target price is clearly aligned with the target population and device value to stakeholders. (It is a common error to set price based on a smaller target population with a high unmet need, but set sales projections based on a broader population.)

- Reimbursement can likely be obtained at the target price.

- The device provides a reasonable value for money (cost-effectiveness).

- The device is affordable to payers or purchasers – that is, the budget impact is manageable.

If several of these statements cannot be supported, the product may not be suitable for further development. There are many case studies of products whose failure in the marketplace could have been predicted and mitigated through this process.

The value proposition should be established globally and refined, adapted, and updated as needed regionally. It is critical that this proposition is aligned with the marketing plan for the device, which will include product/brand messaging that overlaps substantially with the value proposition. The primary differences in these tools is that the product value proposition emphasizes evidence-based value, quantitative measures, and includes sections specific to nontraditional audiences, such as payers, purchasers, and HTA groups.

**FIGURE 4.5 | Framework for a product value proposition.**

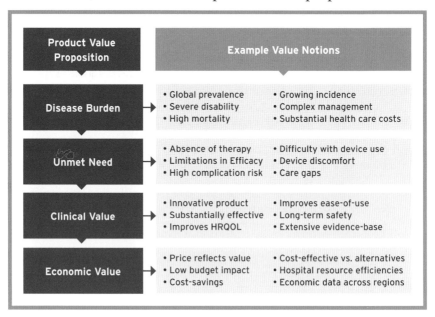

*Figure 4.5* provides a framework for elements in a value proposition that can be used to develop evidence-based and/or product attribute-based value messages for medical devices.

### 4.2.4 MARKETING AND COMMUNICATION TOOLS

Once the value proposition and evidence base for the medical device are developed, they will serve as the basis for the critical tools to be used for internal and external communications. These tools are further described in *Table 4.2*, and how they can be used is discussed in detail in the COMMUNICATE phase.

**TABLE 4.2 |** Internal and external value-based communication tools.

- **Traditional sales and marketing tools** (e.g., product brochures, training packages, detail aids for use with hospitals and physicians) in compliance with regulatory guidelines.

- **Abstracts** and **publications** tailored to multidisciplinary audiences.

- **Internal global value dossiers (GVDs)/value messages,** which are comprehensive documents that serve as a repository of knowledge that is integrated with key value statements for the product.

- **External payer value dossiers** which are typically 20–30 pages and focussed on payers, purchasers, and HTA groups. Depending on the product, Academy of Managed Care Pharmacy and WellPoint dossiers may also be created for the U.S. market.

- **BIAs** and **cost-effectiveness** models that are customizable and for use by regional teams to internally prepare for submission and discussions.

- **Interactive models** that demonstrate budget impact, cost offsets, hospital efficiencies, or cost-effectiveness. These models can be very successful tools for field-based teams' demonstration of value to external customers.

## 4.2.5 TIMING OF ACTIVITIES

The timing of BUILD phase activities is driven by launch sequence and the needs of local markets for support. By 18–24 months before a product's launch, all major markets should be apprised of its expected value proposition, evidence generation activities, and market access and pricing strategies. Updates should be provided at six-month intervals or as major revisions and advances occur. Final versions of the market access strategy, device value proposition, GVD, supplemental product evidence, CEA, BIA, and communication tools should be provided to the lead country 6–12 months before launch, as per local requirements. However, as discussed in the RE-ASSESS section, these materials will undergo continual enhancements throughout the global device launch and post-launch marketing periods.

## 4.3 | COMMUNICATE at Launch

**COMMUNICATE:** The objective of this phase is to communicate the evidence-based and/or product attribute-based value proposition for the medical device to customers and other stakeholders to create awareness of the device, generate demand by clinicians, and gain adoption by payers and hospital purchasing committees.

**FIGURE 4.6 | The COMMUNICATE phase (launch): Description of objectives and activities.**

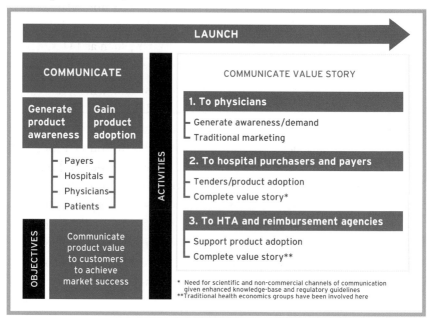

After developing evidence- or product attribute-based communication tools, establishing a price, and obtaining market approval, companies need to communicate the value of the medical device to customers and stakeholders (see *Figure 4.6*). Such communication should reflect the metrics and terminology being adopted by customers, such as comparative effectiveness, budget impact, and cost-effectiveness.

Local regulatory rules need to be considered in the preparation and use of communication tools. For example, Section 114 of the Food and Drug Administration Modernization Act provides draft guidance on the use of promotional materials that comprise health care economic information (HCEI).[29] HCEI is defined as analysis that identifies, measures, or compares economic consequences and includes cost-effectiveness and cost-benefit analyses. The draft guidance specifies that health economics data on an approved indication can be provided to formulary committees and similar groups (HTA committees). The guidance excludes the provision of such data to individual clinicians making patient treatment decisions.[29] The guidance recognizes the unique training and capabilities required of formulary and related committees to evaluate health economics data.[29] It should be noted that this guidance does not apply, at least currently, to CER, such as ITCs, which do not consider product costs or cost-effectiveness.

The unique aspects of health economics data will often mean that the device company will require a specialized team with unique training (e.g., CER, health economics) and highly analytical skill-sets to develop the strategies and materials for such communications and to manage the communication process. In contrast, sales and marketing personnel are often trained and equipped to communicate product promotional material to physicians, rather than highly technical/analytical scientific data and methodologies to payers and purchasers. As well, the need for a specialized HE team may be partly driven by limitations associated with having sales representatives communicate health economic data to customers such as hospital TAC.

## 4.3.1 COMMUNICATE TO PHYSICIANS

Communicating the value proposition to physicians increases product awareness and adoption. Evidence, such as clinical trial data, is incorporated within traditional marketing materials (e.g., product brochures, training packages, detail aids for use with hospitals and physicians) and activities (e.g., training specialists and crafting promotional materials according to regulatory compliance with FDA-approved labeling).[30] These activities are primarily focused on increasing awareness of a product and gaining market share.

As indicated in the previous chapter, physicians are now much more limited in choosing devices due to hospital purchasers taking on a more prominent role.[31] This may be particularly apparent with products that have significant competition or poor differentiation. However, regarding highly innovative products, it can be postulated that physician influence will remain very important to product adoption, as physicians are most likely to drive awareness and uptake of the new technology.

While communication of clinical trial and product attribute data is common in sales and marketing activities, there is value in communicating other aspects of product value to physicians. For example, physicians are increasingly consumers and producers of data on the comparative effectiveness of products, including meta-analyses, ITCs and systematic reviews. In addition, many physicians are now familiar with health economics and the use of cost-effectiveness and budget impact analyses. Again, provision of such data needs to be in compliance with local regulatory requirements.

Useful tools in the communication of the full value of a device to clinicians include publications and detail aids on comparative effectiveness, cost-effectiveness, hospital efficiencies, and budget impact. These materials may be developed at a local level from the product dossier or developed by the global team. Interactive models for demonstrating device impact have also been used extensively for a number of products. These tools may be laptop, Internet, or iPad based, allowing analyses of clinical and economic outcomes that are customized for the population in a physician's practice.

It is important to note that use of comparative effectiveness and economic data and tools with clinicians will need to be compliant with local regulations.

## 4.3.2 COMMUNICATE TO PAYERS AND HOSPITALS

Payers and hospitals comprise the primary audience for the activities described in this chapter. Essentially, payers and hospital purchasers want to understand product value beyond safety and efficacy. Manufacturers who anticipate payer/purchaser concerns and requirements will be at a significant competitive advantage when involved in tenders and negotiations. In general, the evidence generated in the BUILD phase will be used to meet the evaluation requirements of these customers, including the new and evolving HTA committees, as well as support negotiations and potential objections to proposed product price. The specific interactions with such groups may include:

- Negotiations for reimbursement and price setting with payers and hospitals.
- Creation of new reimbursement codes.
- Response to tender requests by hospital groups.
- Payer submissions incorporating the GVD, cost-effectiveness model, and budget impact model.
- Discussion of hospital efficiencies and budget impact, such as cost offsets associated with using the new medical device versus comparators. Such models can be customized according to unique hospital parameters, so that a detailed understanding of budget impact can be gained.
- Response to private insurers' initiatives[32] to roll out value-based payments on a wide scale

Negotiation of risk-sharing agreements with hospitals/payers includes providing coverage based on methods that reduce payer risk or requiring further evidence generation.

The primary tools for communicating the value proposition to these audiences are the payer dossier, publications, CER, cost-effectiveness models/publications, and BIAs. Given the pivotal role payers and purchasers can play in product adoption, the opportunity cost for being unable to rapidly and efficiently respond to concerns of these stakeholders is substantial.

It is important to note that traditional channels of communication with these stakeholders through sales and marketing may not be appropriate.[29,33,34,35] For example, in relation to pharmaceuticals, provision of an AMCP dossier to health care decision makers needs to be based on an unsolicited request[v] and guidance stipulates responses to such requests need to be generated by medical/scientific personnel who are independent of sales and marketing.[35] Scenarios similar to this for medical devices may preclude the use of a traditional sales force and also require scientific channels of communication independent of sales and marketing. Such a specialized HE team will require a unique skill set and knowledge base needed to interpret and communicate CER and health economics data. The team will be interacting with sophisticated, multidisciplinary groups, such as national, regional, and HTA committees whose members are experts in such areas.

In addition to communicating value propositions to hospital decision makers, there is expected to be continued use of customized pricing constructs in contracting processes. This may include consideration of such factors as hospital financial position (e.g., average margin on procedures involving the device) and vendor factors (e.g., quality of service, volume purchased).[36]

### 4.3.3 COMMUNICATE TO NATIONAL/REGIONAL HTA AND REIMBURSEMENT AGENCIES

As discussed in *Chapters 2* and *3*, HTA and reimbursement agencies are charged with evaluating the evidence regarding comparative effectiveness and in some jurisdictions cost-effectiveness. Their decisions regarding product value can dictate the rate of product adoption in a region or country. National and regional agencies may influence technology adoption either at a policy level or at the level of payers and purchasers.

For example, screening technology adoption is strongly impacted by HTA review. The movement of cervical cancer screening in the past decade to human papillomavirus testing was driven in large part by HTA reviews and studies that eventually influenced clinical guidelines.[37,38,39] Similarly, the resistance to movement from conventional

---

[v] **Unsolicited request:** can be defined as a request that is initiated by persons independent of the manufacturer and not prompted by the manufacturer in any way (according to the FDA guidance for industry on responding to unsolicited requests for off-label information about prescription drugs and medical devices)

cytology to liquid-based cytology was influenced greatly by HTA review.[38] The literature contains numerous other examples of device reviews, which could have a substantial impact on adoption. For example, the positive PleurX review by NICE,[40] which found evidence for improved clinical outcomes, decreased complications, improved HRQOL, and cost savings to the payer, is likely to increase adoption of the device by hospitals and payers.

In the United Kingdom (UK), the interest in medical device HTA has resulted in the recent development of the National Institute for Health and Clinical Excellence (NICE) Medical Technology Evaluation Program.[41] MTEP was established to advise to the National Health Service (i.e., public payer in UK) on the adoption of medical devices and diagnostic tests. MTEP's review will be based on comprehensive clinical and economic evaluations conducted by manufacturers, as well as its own assessment.

Some agencies function within or closely to a payer or purchaser, in which case their support can be critical to subsequent adoption of the device. For example, in 2011 BlueCross BlueShield's Technology Assessment Center issued assessments of a number of procedures requiring medical devices, including transcranial magnetic stimulation and artificial vertebral disc arthroplasty, neither of which met the Center's criteria.[42,43]

In all the examples above, the medical device industry has the opportunity to play an active role.[44] It can help shape reviews by anticipating the needs and concerns of HTA groups through the ASSESS process and by providing compelling evidence of device value through the BUILD process. The industry can serve as the evidence generation center by integrating appropriate clinical endpoints within trials, conducting CER, collecting HRQOL and economic data, and examining long-term outcomes through disease simulation modeling. Manufacturers produce or sponsor the vast majority of evidence, which places them in an optimal position to aid agencies in the most appropriate interpretation and utilization of product data. All of these data need to be communicated to decision makers through a number of channels, including conferences, peer-reviewed journals, formal submissions, and presentations. Manufacturers have substantial in-house HTA expertise and capacity, with experience that frequently extends globally. The regulatory and reimbursement processes undertaken by industry, as well as technical modeling expertise, provide important perspectives on regional assessment requirements that may be shared with agencies to improve and expedite HTA review.

The role of HTA in device review and adoption, underscores the importance of a strong internal team and process for assessing, building, and communicating product value using HTA methods.

## 4.4 | Continually ASSESS, BUILD, COMMUNICATE, and DEFEND post-launch

The objective of this phase is to maintain or improve price, value, and reimbursement for continued successful market access for medical devices after their launch.

Once a product is launched, it is important to continuously re-evaluate prior assessments, evidence development, and communication efforts to ensure optimal solutions (see *Figure 4.7*). At a minimum, post-launch should encompass a multi-year process, where discussion with individual payers may lead to an iterative process and where continued access to the most up-to-date evidence and value messaging can be instrumental to regional efforts to secure access. This multi-year process also reflects that evidence generation for a product often produces a great deal of data within the first few years of the product's launch. As such, this evidence will require integration into both the product value proposition and the market access strategy.

It is also important to note that medical device pricing, coverage, reimbursement, and adoption are dynamic over the device's life cycle. Device prices are likely to change over time because of the entry of new products, iterative developments, or variation in how devices are procured in different health care systems.[8,9] Regarding reimbursement of medical devices, there are often updates to coverage decisions and payment amounts. With the highly competitive device market,

**FIGURE 4.7 | The Post-Launch phase: Description of objectives and activities.**

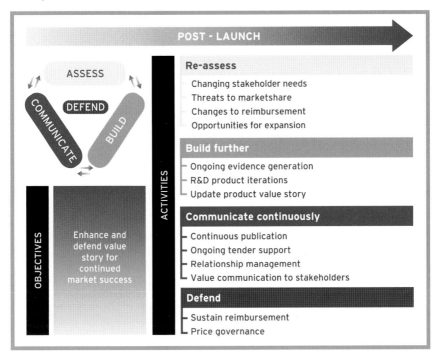

manufacturers may lose market share, whereby hospitals adopt newer products in favor of better pricing and value, and reduce purchasing of others. Therefore, in this dynamic device market, there is a need for continuous strategic re-assessment, evidence generation, stakeholder communication, and defense of pricing and reimbursement. The continual re-evaluation and updating of the evidence and value proposition will also ensure that the company can react to opportunities and challenges that arise in the market.

### 4.4.1 RE-ASSESS

The objective here is to re-asses market opportunities and the value proposition for the product. The checklist in *Table 4.3* provides a guide to the post-launch Re-Assess phase.

Depending on the answers to these questions, there may be opportunities for market expansion or the need for defensive strategies. At a minimum, this phase should be considered quarterly in the first three years post-launch and at least once a year during the bulk of the

**TABLE 4.3 | Checklist of key questions that need to be evaluated as part of the RE-ASSESS phase post-launch.**

### Evidence

- [ ] Has new clinical evidence been generated that supports the current or new indications for the device?
- [ ] Have any new HTA or CER reports been published that raise new questions or provide new support?
- [ ] Are new data for competitors available?
- [ ] Are new studies planned and do they provide an opportunity to address any market opportunities or hurdles?
- [ ] Are CER, CEA and BIA studies up to date?
- [ ] Are device revisions planned that may address limitations (e.g., ease of use) or unmet need (e.g., subpopulation)?

### Competition

- [ ] Are competitors entering the market? Is the comparative value of the device well established and communicated?
- [ ] Does the success against competing devices vary by region or payers? If so, can this be addressed?

### Reimbursement and Access

- [ ] Are there concerns raised by HTA / reimbursement groups that can be addressed by analysis, data collection, or communication?
- [ ] Have policies for the reimbursement of the device changed?
- [ ] Have customer needs or processes changed? Have new customers or stakeholders emerged?
- [ ] To support current and emerging needs of customers, how can the device value proposition best be enhanced?
- [ ] Can coverage and reimbursement for the procedure/device be reduced or eliminated? What efforts are required to avoid this?
- [ ] What are opportunities for enhancing coverage and reimbursement of the procedure / device? How can this best be facilitated?

### Pricing

- [ ] Is there pressure on price from competitors or payers?
- [ ] What are the best methods for ensuring that medical device pricing remains optimal across regions and countries?

product life cycle. Such activities will not only maximize adoption and sales of the current device, they will also inform product development discussions and lay the groundwork for new iterations of the device.

## 4.4.2 BUILD FURTHER

Ongoing evidence generation is essential to continuously demonstrating the clinical and economic advantages of the medical device compared to the most relevant alternative(s). This concept is well established in the clinical development program, where post-launch trials to expand indication, provide longer-term data, expand experience with the device, or fill other evidence gaps are common. Just as in the development stage, there is value in evaluating how these programs can be modified to optimize their use with payers, purchasers, and other decision makers.

In the absence of evidence, price cannot be sustained. The building phase after device launch needs to be dynamic but often focuses on a few key areas:

- **Clinical data collection as noted above**
- **Comparative effectiveness research**
  - Systematic reviews, ITCs, and other CER studies need to be continually updated as new clinical evidence is developed for the device and its competitors.
  - New CER may be required to address studies generated by competitors for their products or by HTA organizations.
- **Economic analyses**
  - All economic analyses will require refinement for the inclusion of new data, competitors, pricing, payers, and policies. This includes CEAs and BIAs.
  - As launch progresses, analysis of payers in each market will be required.

- **Written and interactive tools**

  - Global dossiers, payer and purchaser dossiers, and other written materials should be updated to reflect new data, competitors, and other market issues.

  - New written and interactive materials should be continuously developed to provide new opportunities and avenues for communicating value.

In general, updates to the written materials and evidence base should be considered annually for the first three years post-launch and every one to three years thereafter.

### 4.4.3 COMMUNICATE CONTINUOUSLY

Continuous communication serves multiple purposes: it helps to keep the device top-of-mind to the stakeholder, it reinforces the product value, it provides new evidence of value, and it addresses market challenges.

As new evidence is generated throughout the medical device life cycle, it is critical to clearly and convincingly communicate to various customers and stakeholders using these latest data. Similarly, as requests for tenders will often be issued periodically, companies need to be ready to respond with the latest information supporting product value according to customer needs. Continued assistance may also be needed by purchasers to ensure smooth implementation, maximum clinical value, and up-to-date training. To maintain product awareness and interest, physicians need to be aware of the latest publications and conference presentations differentiating product value. Finally, evidence may be requested as part of communications with customers, such as CMS, whereby reimbursement is contingent on further evidence generation.[45]

### 4.4.4 DEFEND PRICE

For the medical device market, there is a need to consistently monitor global pricing dynamics. Changes to the product value proposition (e.g., performance versus competition), reimbursement, and market factors (e.g., competition price, external price referencing,[w] parallel trade[x,46]) can impact the price hospitals are willing to pay for devices. Such factors must be considered collaboratively through a global pricing strategy that is maintained after the initial price is available.

An ideal price management system allows price transparency, enables clear communication of pricing strategy throughout the organization, assesses price performance at global and local levels, evaluates price impact, monitors reimbursement dynamics, and collates current information pertaining to pricing factors (e.g., value, market, financial). Most important, such a system should involve regular monitoring of sales processes to ensure incentives are aligned with target average sales price[y] when selling to customers.

A global price management system should also have the goal of preserving the global price of a product by providing affiliates with pricing targets and evaluations of the pricing impact throughout the product life cycle. Such methods may help to limit the negative impact of important challenges to the industry, such as parallel import and price referencing. For example, France reviews prices in the UK, Spain, Germany, and Italy as a main criterion in its price-setting process.[47] If a product's price is particularly low due to avoidable factors in any one of these countries, such suboptimal pricing will also be reflected in France. In summary, if a company is not disciplined about price maintenance, it is only a matter of time before the product becomes unprofitable, with resultant loss to investors and consequences to patients due to eventual discontinuation of the device.

Coronary stenting is an important example where changes to the pricing of "older" technology (i.e., BMS) affected pricing for "newer" technology (i.e., DES). For example, NICE's appraisal of DES versus

---

[w] **External price referencing:** The practice of using the price(s) of a health care intervention in one or several countries in order to derive a benchmark or reference price for the purpose of setting the price of the intervention in a given country (European Pharmaceutical Pricing and Reimbursement Information glossary).

[x] **Parallel trade:** Exists when there are significant price differences between countries. Parallel trade occurs when products protected by patent, trademark, or copyright are first placed into circulation in one market, then (re-) imported into a second market without the authorization of the original owner of the intellectual property right .

[y] **Average sales price:** This price is based on manufacturer-reported actual selling price data, often reflects price discounts, and is often publicly available.

BMS negatively impacted the price of DES in the UK,[9] which compromised the price of DES in other countries through price referencing and parallel export.

### 4.4.5 DEFEND REIMBURSEMENT

Reimbursement, often tied to product price, is not ensured throughout the product life cycle. Medical device companies must be aware of changing coverage and reimbursement policies, as well as evolving data needs to support the sustainability of reimbursement for the procedure/device. For instance, the New York Medicaid Review Group recommended that percutaneous coronary intervention (PCI) procedures not be covered any longer for patients with stable coronary artery disease. This decision, which will impact companies with devices used in PCI,[48] was based on the fact that there were insufficient data demonstrating a clear benefit of PCI over medical therapy in this population. This decision may have been avoided through the development of additional studies showing incremental benefits of PCI in this population.

### REFERENCES

1. PAREXEL [Press Release]. Paraxel global survey results identify top concerns of biopharma industry in achieving commercial success. March 15, 2012. Available at: http://www.parexel.com/news-and-events/parexel-news/2012/parexel-global-survey-results-identify-top-concerns-of-biopharma. [Accessed on: March 23, 2012].
2. Booz & Company & National Analysts Worldwide Research Consulting. Pharmaceutical sales and marketing trends 2011. February 2012. Available at: http://www.booz.com/media/uploads/BoozCo-Pharmaceutical-Sales-Marketing-Trends-National-Analysts-2011.pdf. [Accessed on: March 23, 2012].
3. Reaven NL. Health economic data strengthens strategic decisions and product marketing. *BBI Newsletter* 2000. Available at: http://www.strathealth.com/bbi_3.html. [Accessed on: April 23, 2012].
4. Centers for Medicare & Medicaid Services. Overview of ICD-9-CM coding. Available at: http://www.cms.gov/ICD9ProviderDiagnosticCodes/01_overview.asp. [Accessed on: March 23, 2012].
5. Leon MB, et al. Transcatheter aortic-valve implantation for aortic stenosis in patients who cannot undergo surgery. *N Engl J Med* 2010; 363(17):1597-607.
6. Nainggolan L. [Press Release] Two new TAVI devices debut at surgery meeting. October 4, 2011. Available at: http://www.theheart.org/article/1290089.do. [Accessed on: March 23, 2012].
7. Kong DF, et al. Economic impact of drug-eluting stents on hospital systems: A disease-state model. *Am Heart J* 2004;147:449–56.
8. Sorensen C, et al. Applying health economics for policy decision making: Do devices differ from drugs? *Europace* 2011;13:ii54-8.
9. Drummond M, et al. Economic evaluations for devices and drugs – Same or different? *Value Health* 2009; 12(4):402-6.
10. Kramer DB, et al. Regulation of medical devices in the United States and European Union. *N Engl J Med* 2012; 366(9):848-55.

[11] Hutchison CA, et al. Immunoglobulin free light chain levels and recovery from myeloma kidney on treatment with chemotherapy and high cut-off haemodialysis. *Nephrol Dial Transplant* 2012; Jan 23 [Epub ahead of print.]

[12] Hutchison CA, et al. Efficient removal of immunoglobulin free light chains by hemodialysis for multiple myeloma: in vitro and in vivo studies. *J Am Soc Nephrol*, 2007; 3: 886-95.

[13] Saadi R et al. Cost analysis of four major drug-eluting stents in diabetic populations. *Eurointervention*, 2011; 7(3):332-39.

[14] Biondi-Zoccai GG, et al. Adjusted indirect comparison of intracoronary drug-eluting stents: Evidence from a meta-analysis of randomized bare-metal stents controlled trials. *Int J Cardiol* 2005; 100(1):119-23.

[15] Stettler C, et al. Outcomes associated with drug-eluting and bare-metal stents: A collaborative network meta-analysis. *Lancet*. 2007; 370(9591):937-48.

[16] Signorovitch JE, et al. Comparative effectiveness without head-to-head trials: A method for matching-adjusted indirect comparisons applied to psoriasis treatment with adalimumab or etanercept. *Pharmacoeconomics* 2010; 28(10):935-45.

[17] Lane SS. Correction of high myopia with a phakic intraocular lens: Interim analysis of clinical and patient-reported outcomes. *J Cataract Refract Surg* 2011; 37(8):1426-33.

[18] Grima DT, et al. Modelled cost-effectiveness of high cut-off haemodialysis compared to standard haemodialysis in the management of myeloma kidney. *Curr Med Res Opin* 2011; 27(2):383-91.

[19] Marshall DA, et al. Cost-effectiveness of nucleic acid test screening of volunteer blood donations for hepatitis B, hepatitis C, and human immunodeficiency virus in the United States. *Vox Sang* 2004; 86(1):28-40.

[20] Burger EA, et al. Cost-effectiveness of cervical cancer screening with primary human papillomavirus testing in Norway. *Br J Cancer* 2012. [Epub ahead of print.]

[21] Clark MA, et al. Clinical and economic outcomes of percutaneous coronary intervention in the elderly. An analysis of Medicare claims data. *Circulation* 2004; 110:259-64.

[22] Grima DT, et al. Modelled cost-effectiveness of high cut-off haemodialysis compared to standard haemodialysis in the management of myeloma kidney. *Curr Med Res Opin* 2011; 27(2):383-91.

[23] Bernard ML, et al. Economic implications and cost-effectiveness of implantable cardioverter defibrillator and cardiac resynchronization therapy. *Heart Fail Clin* 2011; 7(2):241-50.

[24] Cowie MR, et al. Lifetime cost-effectiveness of prophylactic implantation of a cardioverter defibrillator in patients with reduced left ventricular systolic function: Results of Markov modeling in a European population. *Europace*, 2009; 11(6):716-26.

[25] Saadi R, et al. Cost analysis of vascular closure devices in the United States. Presented at 14th Annual ISPOR Conference, Madrid, Spain; November 5-8, 2011.

[26] Reaven NL. The dilemma of medical device pricing in the USA: Using value-based pricing to support product positioning. *J Med Dev Reg* November 2006; 3(4):26-34. Available at: http://www.strathealth.com/images/pdf/Reaven_JMDRNov06.pdf. [Accessed on: March 27, 2012]

[27] United States Senate, Committee on Finance. Baucus to explore ways to increase price transparency in medical device industry after new report reveals gaps. February 3, 2011. Available at: http://finance.senate.gov/search/?q=Baucus+to+explore+ways+to+increase+price+transparency+in+medical+device+industry+after+new+report+reveals+gaps&access=p&as_dt=i&as_epq=&as_eq=&as_lq=&as_occt=any&as_oq=&as_q=&as_sitesearch=&client=finance&sntsp=0&filter=0&getfields=title&lr=&num=15&numgm=3&oe=UTF8&output=xml&partialfields=&proxycustom=&proxyreload=0&proxystylesheet=default_frontend&requiredfields=&site=finance&sitesearch=&sort=date%3AD%3AS%3Ad1&start=0&ud=1&x=26&y=6. [Accessed on: March 27, 2012]

[28] Suter LG, et al. Medical device innovation – Is "better" good enough? *N Engl J Med* 2011; 365(16):1464-6.

[29] Food and Drug Modernization Act. Promotional use of health care economic information. Guidance for industry.Draft – not for implementation. Available from: http://www.ispor.org/workpaper/ispor_comments/FDA%20draft%20Guidance%20on%20Economic%20Information%20for%20Promotional%20Use.pdf. [Accessed on: April 9, 2012].

[30] National Task force on CME Provider/Industry Collaboration. FDA regulation of promotional activities. 2010; 2(2).

[31] Ernst & Young. Pulse of the industry: Medical technology report. EYGM Limited. 2011; (FN0008) 1107-1271824_SF. Available at: http://www.ey.com/Publication/vwLUAssets/Pulse_of_the_industry/$FILE/Pulse-of-the-industry.pdf. [Accessed on: March 27, 2012]

[32] United Healthcare Services, Inc. Shifting from fee-for-service to value-based contracting model. 2012; UHCEW562088-000. Available at: http://consultant.uhc.com/assets/vbc_overview_flier.pdf. [Accessed on: March 27, 2012]

33 Neumann PJ, et al. How will FDA's new draft guidance on unsolicited requests for off-label information affect AMCP dossiers and the communication of health economic information? Presented at ISPOR 17th Annual International Meeting, Washington, DC. June 2-6, 2012; IP4. Available at: http://www.ispor.org/meetings/washingtondc0512/issue_panels.asp. [Accessed on: March 27, 2012]

34 U.S. Food and Drug Administration. Guidance for industry responding to unsolicited requests for off-label information about prescription drugs and medical devices: Draft guidance. U.S. Department of Health and Human Services, FDA, CDER, CBER, CVM, CDRH. December 2011. Available at: http://www.fda.gov/downloads/Drugs/GuidanceComplianceRegulatoryInformation/Guidances/UCM285145.pdf. [Accessed on: March 27, 2012]

35 Cunningham E, et al. C20: The FDA draft guidance on unsolicited requests for off-label information about prescription drugs and medical devices. AMCP 24th Annual Meeting Expo; April 18-20, 2012. San Francisco, CA.

36 The Advisory Board Company. Navigating the new era of technology assessment. June 17, 2010.

37 Saslow D, et al. American Cancer Society, American Society for Colposcopy and Cervical Pathology, and American Society for Clinical Pathology screening guidelines for the prevention and early detection of cervical cancer. *Am J Clin Pathol* 2012; 137(4):516-42.

38 Whitlock EP, et al. Liquid-based cytology and human papillomavirus testing to screen for cervical cancer: A systematic review for the U.S. Preventive Services Task Force. *Ann Intern Med* 2011 155(10):687-97.

39 Health Council of the Netherlands. Population screening for cervical cancer. Publication no. 2011/07. The Hague, 2011.

40 NICE. MTG9 PleurX peritoneal catheter drainage system for vacuum assisted drainage of treatment-resistant recurrent malignant ascites: Guidance. March 21, 2012.

41 NICE. Medical Technology Evaluation Programme. November 30, 2011. Available at: http://www.nice.org.uk/aboutnice/whatwedo/aboutmedicaltechnologies/medicaltechnologiesprogramme.jsp. [Accessed on: March 27, 2012].

42 Blue Cross and Blue Shield Association. Technology Evaluation Center Assessment Program: Transcranial magnetic stimulation for depression. Kaiser Permanente. July 2011; 26(3):1-28. Available at: http://www.bcbs.com/blueresources/tec/vols/26/26_3.pdf. [Accessed on: April 10, 2012].

43 Blue Cross and Blue Shield Association. Technology Evaluation Center Assessment Program: Artificial intervertebral disc arthroplasty for treatment of degenerative disc disease of the cervical spine. Kaiser Permanente. November 2011; 26(5):1-28. Available at: http://www.bcbs.com/blueresources/tec/vols/26/26_05.pdf. [Accessed on: April 10, 2012].

44 Joint Healthcare Industry Paper. The value of industry involvement in HTA. January 12, 2011. Available at: http://www.efpia.eu/Content/Default.asp?PageID=559&DocID=12342. [Accessed on: March 27, 2012]

45 Mohr P, et al. The comparative effectiveness research landscape in the United States and its relevance to the Medicare Program. Center for Medical Technology Policy. May 31, 2010. Available at: http://htaiced.files.wordpress.com/2011/02/cer-and-ced-in-medicare.pdf. [Accessed on: March 27, 2012]

46 Bart TN. Parallel trade of pharmaceuticals: A review of legal, economic, and political aspects. *Value Health* 2008; 11(5): 996-1005.

47 Leopold C, et al. Differences in external price referencing in Europe: A descriptive overview. *Health Policy* 2012; 104:50-60.

48 New York State Department of Health, Medicaid Redesign Team. Basic Benefit Review Work Group. Final recommendations. November 1, 2011. Available at: http://www.health.ny.gov/health_care/medicaid/redesign/docs/basic_benefit_review_wrk_grp_final_rpt.pdf. [Accessed on: March 27, 2012]

# CHAPTER 5

# The Health Economics Team - Key to Market Access Success

## KEY MESSAGE:

The Health Economics (HE) team plays a key role in the successful execution of the solution described in Chapter 4. This team is central to the development of the product's value strategy, evidence generation, strategic pricing, and market access, and the creation of tools for demonstrating and communicating value. However, these activities should not occur independent of other functions. Strategic opportunities can be maximized by aligning the HE team with the Research & Development (R&D) and Commercial teams.

The opportunity costs of an undeveloped, decentralized, or fragmented health economics function are substantial. A company with a well-developed HE team and process will enjoy a competitive advantage through its ability to foresee market opportunities, avoid hurdles, create global efficiencies, and quickly respond to new market opportunities and challenges.

## CONCEPTS DISCUSSED:

- Definition of health economics and role of an HE team.
- Interdependent responsibilities that fall under health economics: (1) value strategy, (2) evidence generation, (3) tool development, (4) reimbursement, and (5) strategic pricing.
- Opportunity costs associated with underdeveloped HE groups.

As presented in *Chapter 4,* an integrated strategy for achieving market access success involves a series of activities within each product development and commercialization phase that are organized under the categories of ASSESS, BUILD, and COMMUNICATE. The current chapter illustrates the critical role that Health Economics (HE) teams play in this strategy, their alignment with other core industry functions, and the efficiencies realized in a centralized health economics function.

## 5.1 | The Central Role of the HE Team

The term health economics can be variably interpreted within the health care industry. As defined in *Chapter 2,* health economics is the discipline that deals with the application of economic principles and theories to health and the health sector. This discipline is driven by scarcity: health care is limited, and therefore choices have to be made regarding the selection of therapies and devices for use.[1] To optimize health with the given resources available, efficiency[a] must be maximized – a concept often referred to by health economists as the "third step of evidence" after efficacy and effectiveness. For health care interventions, such as medical devices, this often involves assessing whether they provide value for money and are, therefore, an efficient use of limited resources available.[1]

*Figure 5.1* further describes several responsibilities within a company's HE team. Because these responsibilities are closely linked, they should fall under one departmental structure to optimize efficiency and financial gain. In brief, the establishment and compilation of the product value proposition can be supported by the responsibilities of *Value Strategy, Evidence Generation,* and *Tool Development.* Considering product value as part of the price-setting process is an important

---

[a] **Efficiency:** in health care refers to when money spent on an intervention is money spent well. In other words, if it were possible to achieve greater health gains in any area of health with the same money by spending it on something else, the intervention examined is relatively inefficient. The crucial metric is the ratio between the cost needed to carry out the intervention and its health effects, often referred to as the cost-effectiveness ratio.[1]

component of the Strategic Pricing responsibility. Finally, the *Reimbursement* responsibility involves communicating product value in relation to price to achieve optimal access by payers and hospital purchasers. In the case of *Evidence Generation*, historically this has comprised the core of the activities conducted by an HE team. However, with the growing importance of payer and purchaser decision making, the HE team's role has expanded into early strategy phases and later communication phases to optimize market success.

**FIGURE 5.1 | General responsibilities and interdependencies of an industry Health Economics team.**

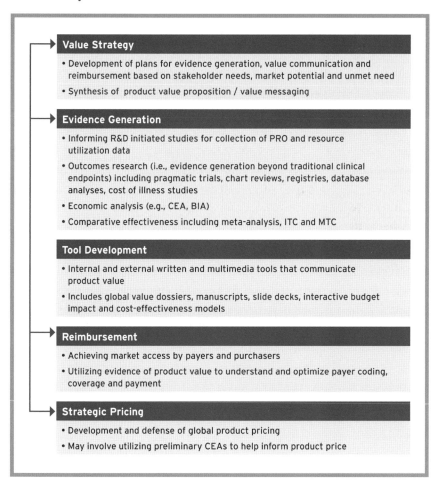

**Value Strategy**

- Development of plans for evidence generation, value communication and reimbursement based on stakeholder needs, market potential and unmet need
- Synthesis of product value proposition / value messaging

**Evidence Generation**

- Informing R&D initiated studies for collection of PRO and resource utilization data
- Outcomes research (i.e., evidence generation beyond traditional clinical endpoints) including pragmatic trials, chart reviews, registries, database analyses, cost of illness studies
- Economic analysis (e.g., CEA, BIA)
- Comparative effectiveness including meta-analysis, ITC and MTC

**Tool Development**

- Internal and external written and multimedia tools that communicate product value
- Includes global value dossiers, manuscripts, slide decks, interactive budget impact and cost-effectiveness models

**Reimbursement**

- Achieving market access by payers and purchasers
- Utilizing evidence of product value to understand and optimize payer coding, coverage and payment

**Strategic Pricing**

- Development and defense of global product pricing
- May involve utilizing preliminary CEAs to help inform product price

These responsibilities of an HE team in collaboration with other industry functions (e.g., marketing and sales) will deliver the solution for market access success proposed in *Figure 4.1* of the previous chapter.

Several activities of the ASSESS phase fall under the HE team's *Value Strategy* responsibility (e.g., assessing evidence needs, market potential, and processes of hospital purchasers), as do the BUILD phase activities for *Strategic Pricing* and *Reimbursement.* Also, the majority of the BUILD activities are included in the *Evidence Generation* and *Tool Development* responsibilities. These responsibilities of an HE team would be required from pre-launch to post-launch, given the continuous need for reassessment and further building of the value proposition/evidence.

Regarding the COMMUNICATE phase, a cross-functional approach is required. In today's changed environment, new customers such as payers and hospital purchasers seek data beyond traditional endpoints (e.g., comparative effective research (CER), cost-effectiveness analysis (CEA)), demand a price that reflects product value, and need to be managed using communication tools that fully and clearly reflect product value. Historically, the role of the HE team in communications has focused on health technology assessments (HTAs) and reimbursement agencies. However, as noted earlier, the role of the HE team in communication has become more prominent with hospital purchasers and payers. This is in large part due to the need for scientific and noncommercial channels of communication which reflects an enhanced knowledge base. These integrated efforts of an HE team not only demonstrate its importance prior to product launch, but also underscore its role throughout the product life cycle, particularly with respect to ongoing value demonstration, reimbursement optimization, and price governance.

## 5.2 | The Opportunity Costs of Undeveloped or Underdeveloped HE Teams

Considering the new demands for medical device manufacturers, it is evident that the health economics function is imperative to achieving the integrated steps outlined in *Figure 4.1.* The fundamental principle rests on the core objective of an HE team – to generate and communicate data that demonstrate a product's full clinical and economic value. This proposition needs to be tailored to the unique needs of today's various customers to achieve market access. The health economics function has thus become increasingly critical, as the need for more and better information has grown in all health care sectors, and favorable reimbursement defines success for products and entire organizations.[2]

Despite the increased need, the health economics function is often absent or underdeveloped in medical device companies due to fragmented structures, the lack of perceived need, or inexperience with what should comprise the responsibilities of an HE team. Given new customers' increasing demands, numerous opportunity costs may be associated with an underdeveloped or absent HE team. These costs include:

- Pipelines with poor commercial potential because early product development and in-licensing decisions were based on market forecasts that do not reflect payer and purchaser perspectives.

- Under pricing of devices, with resultant financial loss (and disservice to stockholders), or inconsistent global pricing leading to parallel importation issues.

- Failure to achieve access and reimbursement, with resultant sales and financial losses.

- Loss of regional market opportunities due to a lack of global coordination and resultant late timing of evidence and communication tools.

- Adverse patient consequences due to suboptimal market access.

The use of health economics in pricing, pipeline, and in-licensing decisions is particularly critical. In the absence of dedicated HE team resources, decisions may often be made without considering how the evidence or product value supports pricing and the expected impact on market access and reimbursement. For instance, if a new device is as safe and effective as a competitor's device, but is easier to use and thereby reduces operation room time, it will offer hospitals better value for their money, given the resource efficiencies they can gain. If this evidence is not considered, the product may be priced comparably to its competitor's device, resulting in a financial loss to companies and stockholders due to the missed premium price. Similarly, making product pipeline and in-licensing decisions without consideration of payers and purchasers has led to disappointed shareholders due to ambitious market projections that cannot be met because of restricted market access and reimbursement. With regard to product licensing, selling companies commonly promote the possibility of a high device price and a broad patient population, but in reality price premiums are most often obtained for products with more targeted patient populations. As such, buying companies are at risk of overpaying without due diligence around the intersect of pricing, reimbursement, and market access.

Further, a fragmented department or lack of resources dedicated to reimbursement activities could lead to missed regional market opportunities. As previously discussed, reimbursement evidence and communication needs are clearly different from regulatory needs and vary by region. The role of a global HE team is to provide strategic guidance, value evidence, and communication tools in a timely manner, so as to maximize local opportunities. The absence of a dedicated HE team, whose members are aware of coding, coverage, and payment processes and are integrated within all phases of product development, will jeopardize optimal regional pricing and reimbursement.

Almost as damaging as not conducting global health economic activities are delays in these activities due to a lack of corporate buy-in and funding. It is common for individual countries to initiate projects that duplicate global efforts due to the delays in execution of the global program.

Finally, missed reimbursement opportunities will result not only in companies' experiencing avoidable financial shortfalls, but also in patients' suffering the clinical consequences. Whether patients have private insurance or are publicly supported through national health care systems, they will be impacted by lack of access to innovative technologies. This represents the ultimate cost of failing to obtain adequate market access or reimbursement for a new device.

## 5.3 | Meeting Market Demands with Cross-Functional Alignment

In the past, the role of health economics was narrow, with a focus on evidence development for reimbursement submissions and publications. At that time, product awareness activities, typically generated through traditional sales and marketing teams, were sufficient to drive a device's adoption. With the evolution of new customers, the barriers to adoption have grown. To address these barriers through an expanded product value proposition and targeted research, the role of the HE team has expanded to include earlier strategic planning, greater evidence generation, and later value communication.

In reviewing the proposed solution provided in *Chapter 4*, it is clear that close collaboration among functional disciplines is required now more than ever. Given the significant efforts needed to assess, build, and communicate product value to payers, purchasers, and other stakeholders, companies must build structures that foster innovative thinking, provide synergistic outputs, and align health economics across R&D, commercial, and other company functions.[2,3,4]

> ## Increasing Requirements for Health Economics and Cross-Functional Alignment in the New Value Era for Medical Devices
>
> PAST
> - Market access of medical devices was primarily contingent on regulatory approval and product awareness.
> - Physicians were key decision makers in hospital device selection.
> - R&D and commercial functions were primarily involved.
>
> RECENT
> - Market access of medical devices has become more contingent on payer reimbursement.
> - Hospital economic decision makers (e.g., finance) are becoming more involved in device selection.
> - R&D and commercial functions are still primarily involved.
> - The health economics function has been introduced within the industry with a targeted role.
>
> PRESENT AND FUTURE
> - Market access of medical devices is contingent on showing clinical and economic value primarily to payers, hospitals, and physicians.
> - The health economics function needs to have an integral role in demonstrating and communicating the value of medical devices.
> - Health economics and R&D/commercial functions need to be fully aligned as building and communicating product value requires successful integration of all disciplines.

## 5.3.1 ALIGNING HE WITH R&D TEAMS

For maximum return on investment for a product, the HE team must be involved in the early stages of product development. This will ensure that pre-launch activities address the needs of payers and purchasers, as well as the regulatory authorities. As such, the HE team must be aligned with R&D teams (pre-clinical and clinical) to:

- ensure that the overall product value proposition is supported by evidence that will resonate with payers and purchasers;
- identify clinical endpoints for collection that may drive budget impact or cost-effectiveness analyses;
- guide collection of patient-reported outcome, health-related quality of life (HRQOL), resources use, and cost data; and

• provide guidance on market potential based on target population and value-based pricing.

In particular, alignment is needed during the early pre-market phase to maximize opportunities for early data collection and strategic discussion regarding whether the access or reimbursement hurdles may substantially impede market potential. Where appropriate, economic, and humanistic (e.g., HRQOL) endpoints should also be collected from early clinical trials to gain a head start in developing the full product value proposition and inform price-setting strategies.

## 5.3.2 ALIGNING HE WITH COMMERCIAL TEAMS

The post-launch customer base for a device has expanded to include a wide range of stakeholders who work in collaborative systems to influence adoption, access, and reimbursement decisions. Given this network of decision makers, the value proposition must be consistent between the HE and Commercial teams. This will require cross-functional training and communication, with the goal of aligning the HE team's product value proposition with the Commercial team's marketing messages and materials.

Such alignment will help the Commercial team understand what type of information is available within and beyond trial data, and communicate such evidence in accordance with regulatory guidance. For example, Section 114 of the Food and Drug Administration Modernization Act provides guidance on the use of promotional materials that comprise health economics information.[5] The guidance specifies that health economics data on an approved indication may be provided to formulary committees and similar groups (HTA committees), but not to individual clinicians making patient treatment decisions.

The unique aspects of health economics data will often mean that the device company will require a specialized team with unique training (e.g., CER, health economics) and highly analytical skill-sets to develop the strategies and materials for such communications and to manage the communication process. In contrast, sales and marketing personnel are often trained and equipped to communicate product promotional material to physicians, rather than highly technical/analytical scientific data and methodologies to payers and hospital purchasers. As well, the need for a specialized HE team may be partly driven by limitations associated with having sales representatives communicate health economic data to customers such as hospital TAC.

The HE team will also work with the Commercial teams to provide additional product evidence, including budget impact, to support tender negotiations by payers and purchasers. Further, alignment will be needed to establish efficient protocols for review of health economics evidence and materials by all necessary departments.

Finally pricing activities will require substantial collaboration. As discussed earlier, the pricing process traditionally includes data provided by Commercial teams, including market- and financial-based factors. The strategic pricing process combines such knowledge with HE team input from value-based pricing research and review of the global reimbursement environment. This will provide a pricing strategy that both reflects payer and purchaser restrictions and achieves commercial objectives.

### 5.3.3 OPTIMIZING ORGANIZATIONAL STRUCTURE

In terms of organizational structure and reporting, the HE team should be positioned as a department on the same level as the Commercial and R&D departments, reporting to common senior personnel. In addition, the health economics leadership should be part of senior management and involved in key company decision making. *Figure 5.2* illustrates a simplified schematic of the independent setup and cross-functional alignment recommended, which is based on a proven structure that has helped companies achieve market access success and financial targets in the current medical device landscape.

**FIGURE 5.2** | Simplified schematic illustrating the ideal implementation and alignment of a health economics department in relation to other core company functions.

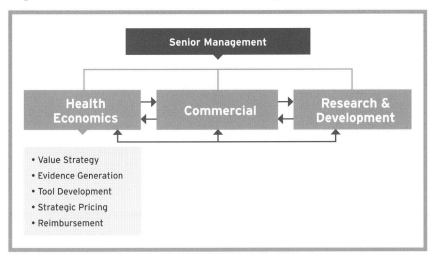

## 5.4 | Improving Efficiencies through Centralized Market Access Strategies

The creation of the solution outline in *Chapter 4* requires centralization of market access strategies across regions and product categories. Given the increasing hospital and payer customer base, such integration will be essential to maximizing the efficiency of internal resources and executing a consistent strategy. Such centralization would ideally involve development of the key strategies, methodologies, and global templates, with implementation and adaptation occurring on a regional/local level. A centralized program will create several efficiencies:

- Strategy and messaging across the company can become consistent.

- Gold standards for market access tools (e.g., budget-impact models, value dossiers) can be established with adherence to developed practices. Such high-level tools would not be feasible to develop in small markets working independently due to resource and proximity to early product R&D and commercial function.

- Duplication of efforts for strategy or tool development can be avoided.

- Central databases can be developed (e.g., global price management, reimbursement regulations).

- A smaller pool of high-level researchers and strategists can be used, who can support regional activities.

- Strategy can be developed at a central level, freeing up resources for local implementation.

- Knowledge dissemination (e.g., guidelines, market changes, customer needs, research endeavors, processes) across product divisions and regions can be enhanced.

In addition to these efficiencies, a centralized market access strategy will let customers know what types of evidence, tools, and communications to expect when they interface with company personnel. In this way, product adoption will be promoted both through the relationship between the customer and company representative as well as through evidence-based value communications. This is particularly important as regional HTA and reimbursement groups communicate frequently through public dissemination of decisions, trade publications, journals, and conferences. Inconsistent messages and evidence across regions will be readily apparent and detrimental to relationships with decision makers.

A centralized HE team will also meet the market needs for complex evidence requirements, such as extensive systematic reviews, indirect treatment comparisons (ITCs), and cost-effectiveness analyses. Execution of such activities at a regional level would be impractical and resource intensive. Field-based personnel will need to (1) critically review and expertly communicate the clinical and economic evidence-based value proposition for a medical device; (2) thoroughly understand the evolving needs of local hospital assessment committees, hospital economics, and the coding, reimbursement, and payment processes; and (3) perform customized budget-impact or other model-based analyses.

An integral aspect of centralization is the ability to create a comprehensive repository of knowledge in the forms of databases and people. A common weakness observed across the industry is loss of knowledge. For example, there are numerous case studies of companies that have been unable to adequately respond to requests for information by HTA groups due to a lack of a centralized process for developing, storing, and disseminating ITCs, systematic reviews, and other product evidence. The most advanced device companies can quickly respond to HTA and reimbursement requests and market opportunities (e.g., positive evidence or guidance) and challenges (e.g., changes in policy or new competitors), due to the knowledge base and integration of their teams. As such, the opportunity cost of a decentralized health economics function that is poorly aligned with other company functions is substantial.

## REFERENCES

1   Annemans L. Health economics for non-economists. An introduction to the concepts, methods and pitfalls of health economic evaluation. The Netherlands: Gent. Academia Press, 2008.
2   Cutting Edge Information. Health economics and outcomes research (PH137): US, Europe, Canada and emerging markets. Summary. 2010. Available at: http://www.cuttingedgeinfo.com/research/market-access/health-economics, http://www.cuttingedgeinfo.com/research/market-access/health-economics. [Accessed on: April 3, 2012]
3   Badia X, et al. HTA moves center stage: Early focus key to future success. *Access Point: IMS Health Economics and Outcomes Research* May 2011; 1(2):14-17. Available at: http://www.imshealth.com/imshealth/Global/Content/IMS%20in%20the%20News/Documents/AccessPoint%20issue2%20final.pdf. [Accessed on: April 4, 2012].
4   Keja J. Putting the P into outcomes research: The increasing relevance of PROs. *Access Point: IMS Health Economics and Outcomes Research* May 2011; 1(2):31-5. Available at: http://www.imshealth.com/imshealth/Global/Content/IMS%20in%20the%20News/Documents/AccessPoint%20issue2%20final.pdf. [Accessed on: April 4, 2012].
5   Food and Drug Modernization Act. Promotional use of health care economic information. Guidance for industry. Draft – not for implementation. Available at: http://www.ispor.org/workpaper/ispor_comments/FDA%20draft%20Guidance%20on%20Economic%20Information%20for%20Promotional%20Use.pdf. [Accessed on: April 9, 2012].

# CHAPTER 6

# Final Considerations

## KEY MESSAGE:

The optimal implementation of the proposed solution recommended in previous chapters will require thoughtful and practical consideration in the context of adapting it to any given company based on such factors as region, company size, company position in the market, and product portfolio. Implementation of the solution also requires investment and strategic planning in terms of resources directed toward acquiring talent and generating additional evidence.

## CONCEPTS DISCUSSED:

- Challenges associated with generating new evidence requirements.
- Acquisition of the right talent/skill set to implement solutions.
- Application of solutions to different device categories.
- Opportunities for start-up companies.
- Application to emerging markets.

Implementing this book's recommended solution for achieving market success today and tomorrow will pose initial resource, restructuring, and priority-setting challenges that manufacturers will need to address rapidly. Also, manufacturers will need to consider and adapt this strategy in the context of their size, experience, and product portfolio.

## 6.1 | Meeting the Challenges of New Evidence Requirements

A major portion of today's medical device market demands involves the need for new evidence. Customers want proof that a product is better than the current standard of care, rather than just a placebo. They also want evidence that it provides value for their money, not just clinical value. Data need to demonstrate that the product works well in the real world over the long term and provides outcomes that are favorable to the patient. While acquiring these data will take more effort and resources than in the past, if acquired strategically, the expanded data set will unquestionably provide market opportunities.

The key to addressing resource challenges associated with data generation is ensuring that the process is relevant, timely, and efficient. Data relevance, as discussed in *Chapter 4*, is best achieved by obtaining a comprehensive understanding of different customer requirements and designing research that targets the majority of customers. Regarding timeliness and efficiency, early data collection may save time and resources. For instance, collecting economic parameters within early clinical trials may avoid the need for separate, costly economic studies to be conducted later on and will provide data that economic decision makers will need early in the product's launch. Such early data collection may be essential to avoiding lengthy review periods for certain device classes that delay a product's market introduction.

Furthermore, companies will need to continually assess and develop strategies that will maximize efficiencies with evidence generation. As discussed in previous chapters, this step may include using practical, methodologically sound research designs, such as indirect treatment comparisons for evaluating all relevant comparators, which may take the place of more expensive clinical trials or observational studies. Understanding which research designs are acceptable by different decision makers is essential for this effort. Also, developing global strategic templates and designs (e.g., cost-effectiveness and budget-impact models) that can accommodate accurate and relevant local adaptation will help achieve efficiency. Finally, as discussed in *Chapter 5*, alignment of groups involved in data generation will help to gain efficiencies by avoiding duplication of efforts and synergistically developing a complete product value proposition that will maximize the chances of successful market access.

## 6.2 | Acquiring the Best Talent

The health economics functions will require personnel with hard-to-find skills sets, given the increased complexity of the customer base, evolving data requirements, and specialized research knowledge. These individuals must understand the evolving payer/purchaser environment, the roles of reimbursement, and what information is needed to design appropriate studies and communication tools. A combination of technical excellence and strong communications skills is required to successfully interact with highly technical specialty groups (e.g., health technology assessment, comparative effectiveness research, and reimbursement bodies) and to translate sophisticated research into accessible messages for non-specialist internal and external audiences.

An understanding of several specialties, including medicine, epidemiology, public health, biostatistics, mathematics, pharmacology, and economics, is required in individuals who will fulfill health economic functions. Ideally, knowledge of commercial, health economic, and R&D processes within industry, with a proven ability to link these functions and create successful solutions, is required of senior personnel directing health economic professionals. A current issue for building such a team is the severe skills shortage in this area.[1,2]

The "talent challenge" is not restricted to the medical device industry. Qualified personnel are in high demand for health economic positions within the pharmaceutical industry as well. An Internet search regarding recruitment of health economics skill sets reveals multiple Web sites with numerous positions that are continuously posted. Such global websites include: *healtheconomics.com, ispor.org,* and *indeed.com* to name a few.

In summary, companies may take three routes toward hiring such talent for the medical device industry:[3] (1) train employees who have the suited academic background internally who express interest and passion within the health economics area; (2) recruit graduates at universities specializing in health economics; and (3) hire personnel from the pharmaceutical industry (or consulting firms serving this industry), as this function is better established in that industry. These executives need to receive appropriate training for successful transition from pharmaceuticals to medical devices. Furthermore, if an appropriate training program is in place, companies may be successful in hiring personnel qualified in evaluating epidemiological or clinical research and training them in health economic concepts, principles, and methods.

In addition to recruitment, developing and retaining talent is critical,[1] especially given the health economics skills shortage. Successful retention is clearly based on several factors, including investment in training, employee recognition and leadership opportunities, and competitive compensation packages. However, a strong corporate culture that is highly respected among the scientific community, combined with a strong internal organizational structure that recognizes the importance of health economics in the new market, may be equally as important. The brightest and best of health economists suited to the industry will want to be a part of a company that recognizes and exemplifies the critical need for health economics in market access success. It should be clear to employees that market access is an important function in the company, because it is integrated with other key areas of research and development, marketing, and commercialization, and that a centralized strategy has been developed to facilitate market access. As such, organizational structures that reflect this principle, as proposed in *Chapter 5*, can undoubtedly benefit employee retention.

As noted earlier, the senior health economic team members will be expected to have in-depth understanding of and experience with clinical, commercial, and health economic sectors to be able to successfully strategize and support market access functions. With regard to these individuals especially, it is critical that a centralized function is developed, as it is not anticipated that high-level health economics experience can be developed within every product division or region.

## 6.3 | Applying the Recommended Solutions to Different Device Categories

The recommended solution will require unique considerations according to device type, as processes and evaluation criteria will likely vary by device factors, including the cost of the device; whether capital investment is required (e.g., robots, ultrasound equipment); if it is implantable (e.g., discs, stents, pacemakers); or if it is a less expensive supply (e.g., bandages, sutures, syringes, needles, catheters). Further, criteria may vary according to whether a device is used in diagnosis (e.g., screening test) or in treatment. Finally, the methodological rigor by which devices are evaluated for regulatory approval is highly contingent on their potential for harm, which may also be reflected in adoption processes.[4,5]

For devices that are more costly, have non-negligible human risk, and fall within a competitive market (e.g., abdominal aortic aneurysm stent grafts, carotid stents), it is clear that new evidence needs will apply here. For devices that are extremely costly (i.e., > $1 million), such as robotic surgical devices, but unique and in high demand by surgeons, proof of resource efficiencies (e.g., shorter hospital stays, less hospital resources used, fewer complications, higher volumes generated) will still be critical in justifying price.[6] For example, a recent report indicated that the appropriate positioning of expensive robotic surgical device use within the framework of existing coding policies, as well as the demonstration of potential revenue enhancements, avoided catastrophic reimbursement constraints and allowed better perceived market value.[6]

Finally, for low-cost devices (e.g., sutures, needles, simple catheters), the need for data beyond regulatory approval will be lower than for more costly devices, with the likelihood of market success depending on competition, price, demand, and, importantly, the volume of the product that is required by the institution(s). Companies must balance the costs of additional evidence generation with the predicted return on investment for these types of devices. Clinical trials may tend to be very limited or absent for these products, as they pose low risk and therefore undergo minimal scrutiny from regulatory bodies. Nevertheless, opportunities should be investigated for whether an integrated value proposition would be useful for relevant customers of these products, particularly where competition exists. Such value propositions may not be heavily clinically oriented, however, may involve product-attribute based messaging that utilizes scientific literature to predict clinical and economic benefits. Further, the likelihood of additional data generation may very well depend on the estimated budget impact of the product within the hospital(s). For instance, if high volumes of a low-cost product are needed, resulting in a budget impact of several hundreds of thousands/millions of dollars, and if competition exists, a competitive advantage may exist for a company that has a product value proposition for its device versus a company that does not.

## 6.4 | Helping Start-Up Companies Gain Market Access

The proposed solutions offered in this book are not only intended for established medical device companies. These solutions also apply to start-up companies that in fact may have more to lose if they do not gain market access success for any given product, given their more limited product portfolios. Start-ups also have one other audience for which product value is critical: the investor. The level of investment will be contingent on the product's perceived value. This value will include many of the concepts discussed within the development of a device value proposition – namely, unmet need, clinical performance, patient outcomes, safety, comparative effectiveness, price, reimbursement, cost-effectiveness, and budget impact. It is in the best interest of the start-up company to have addressed as many of these issues as possible in order to more accurately quantify the product's value in the marketplace and, hence, reduce uncertainty for the investor. Conversely, investment groups and larger device companies considering product licensing/purchase are increasingly considering such issues during the due diligence process.

The ASSESS and BUILD phases pre-launch are particularly fundamental to start-up success. The target product profile must be strategically built prior to conducting clinical trials. The guesswork needs to be taken out of determining how a product will fit in the market. Instead, the focus should be on accurately quantifying unmet need. Further, pre-launch reimbursement scanning is essential. As discussed, this may include creation of separate procedure and reimbursement codes if data are supportive, or working with existing codes and payment processes to limit coverage hurdles post-launch. Relevant and timely targeted evidence that will support a high reimbursement potential for the product must be generated with limited resources available. Also pricing potential in reference to the evidence needs to be clearly demonstrated. Once it is clear that an unmet need exists and preliminary evidence supports product value and price potential, then start-up companies will be more likely to achieve success in acquiring further investments for development.

Start-up companies often fail to achieve adequate reimbursement, despite successful regulatory approval. This can be fatal, given the limited product line of small companies. As such, start-up companies must include reimbursement and pricing functions along with clinical and commercial functions within their foundational structure.

## 6.5 | Monitoring Trends in Emerging Markets

The content of this book was written in the context of North American and European markets, given the overarching parallels in the challenges facing their respective health care systems, as well as some of the fundamental adaptation strategies that are currently being implemented by payers and purchasers.

Such adaptation strategies depend to a large extent on economic development. While emerging markets, such as China, India, Brazil, Eastern Europe, and the Middle East, are not currently facing the acuity of the challenges developed countries are facing today, these markets are beginning to experience increasing pressure. Similar catalysts of unsustainable health care expenditures exist in emerging markets (e.g., shift to older populations, increasing life expectancy, and the presence of chronic disease),[7] which cannot be ignored. Further, although product adoption is still primarily based on physician demand in many emerging markets, some countries have started adopting cost containment tools, indicating that more cost control mechanisms are likely to follow.

The medical device industry would be wise to monitor trends in pharmaceutical pricing and reimbursement within these emerging markets, as they may be early predictors for eventual challenges for devices. In general, it is in the best interest of such emerging markets to prepare for future challenges to their sustainability and profitability.

# REFERENCES

[1] Successful recruiting in the medical device industry. *Medical Device & Diagnostic Industry Magazine.* June 1, 1999. Available at: http://www.mddionline.com/article/successful-recruiting-medical-device-industry. [Accessed on: March 13, 2012]

[2] Cutting Edge Information. Health economics and outcomes research (PH137): US, Europe, Canada and emerging markets. Summary. 2010. Available at: http://www.cuttingedgeinfo.com/research/market-access/health-economics, http://www.cuttingedgeinfo.com/research/market-access/health-economics [Accessed on: April 3, 2012]

[3] Hagle U, Woods C, and Korn/Ferry Institute. Europe's medical device industry: Leadership challenges in a changing world. February 2011.

[4] Kramer DB, et al. Regulation of medical devices in the United States and European Union. *N Engl J Med* 2012; 366:848-55.

[5] Government of Canada, Department of Justice. Medical device regulations. November 30, 2011; SOR/98-282. Available at: http://www.emergogroup.com/files/Canada-Medical-Devices-Regulations-v2.pdf. [Accessed on: March 13, 2012].

[6] Sparks J, et al. Reimbursement and coverage strategies matter: Here's why. *Medical Device & Diagnostic Industry Magazine.* December 8, 2011. Available at: http://www.mddionline.com/article/reimbursement-and-coverage-strategies-matter-heres-why. [Accessed on: March 13, 2012].

[7] Lau J. Medical device market: Mega trends in Asia. Asian Hospital and Healthcare Management. 2012. Available at: http://www.asianhhm.com/equipment_devices/medical_device_market.htm. [Accessed on: April 10, 2012].